THE AMERICAN WAY OF LAUGHING is an anthology of essays, short stories and poems that traces the humorous tradition in this country from Benjamin Franklin to Woody Allen. You'll find homespun witticisms of frontier humorists, dialect jokes and malapropisms of rustic philosophers, and tongue-in-cheek self-appraisals by contemporary comedians. The selections range in tone and style from irony, parody and nonsense to black humor and the bizarre. Together, they provide a picture of the changing social, political and personal concerns of Americans throughout our nation's history.

THE AMERICAN WAY OF LAUGHING

* *

HELEN S. WEISS
AND M. JERRY WEISS

BANTAM BOOKS · TORONTO · LONDON · NEW YORK

RLI: $\dfrac{\text{VLM 5 (VLR 4-8)}}{\text{IL 7+}}$

THE AMERICAN WAY OF LAUGHING
A Bantam Book / December 1977

COPYRIGHTS AND ACKNOWLEDGMENTS

The copyright notices are listed below and on the following page, which constitutes an extension of this copyright page.

"The Whistling River," from Ol' Paul the Mighty Logger by Glen Rounds; copyright 1936, 1949 by Holiday House, Inc., renewed © 1976 by Glen Rounds. By permission of Holiday House, Inc.
"The Big Fine," from Mr. Dooley Says by Finley Peter Dunne; copyright 1910 by Charles Scribner's Sons. By permission of the publisher.
"Reno, Nevada" and "Congress," from The Autobiography of Will Rogers by David Day; copyright 1949 by Rogers Company. By permission of Houghton Mifflin Company.
"One Perfect Rose," "Résumé," and "Just a Little One," from The Portable Dorothy Parker; copyright 1926, 1954 by Dorothy Parker. By permission of Viking Penguin, Inc.
"The Rabbits Who Caused All The Trouble," "The Hen and the Heavens," and "The Unicorn in the Garden," from Fables For Our Time by James Thurber; copyright 1940 by James Thurber, renewed © 1968 by Helen Thurber; and "The Night the Ghost Got In," from My Life and Hard Times by James Thurber; copyright 1933, (c) 1961 by James Thurber. All published by Harper & Row, Publishers, Inc., and originally appeared in The New Yorker. By permission of Mrs. James Thurber.
"About Myself," from The Second Tree From the Corner by E. B. White; copyright 1945 by E. B. White. Originally appeared in The New Yorker. By permission of Harper & Row, Publishers, Inc.

This book may not be reproduced in whole or in part, by mimeograph or any other means, without permission. For information address: Bantam Books, Inc.

ISBN 0-553-11105-1

Published simultaneously in the United States and Canada

Bantam Books are published by Bantam Books, Inc. Its trademark, consisting of the words "Bantam Books" and the portrayal of a bantam, is registered in the United States Patent Office and in other countries. Marca Registrada. Bantam Books, Inc., 666 Fifth Avenue, New York, New York 10019.

PRINTED IN THE UNITED STATES OF AMERICA

To our four children—
Sharon, Frann, Eileen and Michael—

the laughter in our lives

Contents

Introduction

From Benjamin Franklin to Woody Allen, American humorists have us laughing at ourselves and the lives we lead. In this still young, self-made nation, humor continues to ring with homespun, good-natured philosophy that speaks to the common man. Because it developed out of our unique national experience, our humor is as characteristically American as our landscape, our flora and our fauna. And our own native ingredients of warmth and hominess combine to give it a special cracker-barrel flavor, endearing to the heart of every reader.

The pieces in this collection were chosen for several reasons. First, they are representative of the variety of American humor as it developed over two hundred years, a sampler of folktales, almanacs, short stories, newspaper columns, fables, poems and essays. Examples of all of these are included in this volume, reflecting two centuries of American humor.

Second, every author in this book is considered a humorist primarily. While many American writers, from Hawthorne, Poe and Melville, to Dos Passos, Wouk and Bellow, have contributed to the comedy classics, we have chosen to concentrate here on those American humorists whose fame rests fundamentally on their ability to make people laugh.

Finally, our choices were based on their timelessness. Language, manners and literary style may vary from one generation to the next, but human nature remains unchanged. Few things show it to better advantage than humor. The practical advice Benjamin Franklin dispenses in *Poor Richard's Almanack* will be as valid two hundred years from today as when he wrote it. Finley P. Dunne's observations in "The Big Fine" remind us that people in high places rarely alter their attitudes. The cantankerous boy in O. Henry's "The Ransom of Red Chief" is the rambunctious, rotten "everykid" of the world. And what teenager doesn't agonize through puberty rites such as those Jean Shepherd describes in "Wanda Hickey's Night of Golden Memories"?

These basic human concerns that are the butt of our humor may remain constant, but each humorist brings to them fresh observations and a very personal view. The humorist's interpretation of changing events and attitudes also serves to reflect a particular epoch in history. The scope of this collection is designed not only to entertain, but to provide insight into our country's social, cultural and political growth.

The earliest comic tradition in America was, for the most part, oral. Jokes and anecdotes were exchanged around the campfires of wagon trains, on riverboats and cowboy trails. Then they were retold around pot-bellied stoves in general stores and trading posts. Over the years, the stories were expanded, exaggerated. In a comparatively short time, they grew into tall tales and legends, developing into a treasure house of American folklore. These early tales thus became the source material for some of our most outstanding humorous writers. Well into the 1800s, the frontier humor of Davy Crockett, Josh Billings, Mark Twain and Will Rogers drew upon these crackerbox yarns.

Benjamin Franklin is generally regarded as America's first literary humorist. His shrewdness, common sense and wit have become mainstays of American humor. Franklin's first funny pieces, the *Dogood Papers*, were actually letters to the editor sent anonymously to his brother's newspaper. Later, *Poor Richard's Almanack*, which, starting in 1732, appeared regularly for twenty-five years, expressed Franklin's philosophy of a simple, honest life. Through proverbs and hints both "entertaining and useful," Franklin taught wisdom with levity and humor.

Rustic, homespun humor flourished through the nineteenth century. Cracker-barrel philosophers plied their wit jabbing at politics, religion and human nature. Anecdotes, sketches, letters and almanacs are the main sources of humor during this period, abounding with dialect spellings and malapropisms that reveal the local color in the stories of our first frontiersmen. And while the oral, storytelling style is preserved by those rustic humorists in their writings, the philosophical concerns they express have a direct link with Franklin.

Alongside this tradition of homespun humor, literary craftsmanship began to surface in the work of such polished writers as O. Henry, Oliver Wendell Holmes and Twain. An uncanny understanding of our nation and its people unites these literary humorists and the cracker-barrel philosophers. The same splendid insight that sparkles beneath the backwoods delivery of Crockett and Billings, shines through the subtly crafted stories of O. Henry, the poetry and essays of Holmes, and Twain's great inventory of sketches and novels.

Twain's lifetime (1835–1910) saw a radical change in America from an agrarian to an industrial society. Population shifted from rural areas to urban centers. The nation grew in wealth and territory. And as day to day life became easier for the individual in terms of material comfort, it became more complex psychologically for society as a whole.

Then, in turn, the twentieth century brought a proliferation of humorous writers who raised high the banner against the intrusive influences in this pressure-cooker society. Contemporary humorists such as Art Buchwald satirize the political and social scene in much the same manner that Billings and Dunne targeted public figures and national institutions. Following the critical tone set by Franklin, Holmes and Twain, they censure the plight of the individual drowning in a sea of complications. Buchwald faces a frustrating dilemma without a driver's license; E. B. White ridicules the "numbers system"; Judith Viorst finds that her most important nemesis is, after all, "Money."

Other vigorous strains of humor have emerged—black humor, notably in the comic work of Langston Hughes; a sense of the bizarre in the writings of James Thurber and comedian Woody Allen. And, significantly, many humorists have moved away from the public sphere and turned inward. These humorists are concerned with defining personal identity in relation to ethnicity, family, manners. White, Dorothy Parker, Jean Kerr, Sam Levenson and Shepherd make us laugh at their personal eccentricities—and ultimately at ours as well.

Oral and literary traditions in humor are very much alive today. Interestingly, most of America's popular literary humorists have been involved with the world of journalism—a medium for which the written and spoken word are both vital. Franklin, Holmes, Billings, Twain, Dunne, Rogers, Thurber, Parker, Hughes, Ogden Nash, White and Buchwald are among the newspaper and magazine reporters, columnists, editors and publishers on the roster of outstanding comic writers. For the performing humorist, the lecture platform, which was so popular in the 1800s, has undergone a partial metamorphosis in converting to the mass media. The advent of radio, films and television has opened unlimited opportunities for humorists as writers, performers, directors and producers. Today they are reaching wider audiences than ever before.

Writing for the media requires techniques quite different from those used by literary humorists in the past. As it moves from the written word to performance, humor must be at once literary, verbal and *visual*. Yet, while the mechanics of multi-media humor differ from those of written humor, their style and subjects are often the same. Television comedy shows and comedy films delight viewers with the same kinds of humor readers continue to appreciate in magazines, newspapers, poems and books.

We hope that the enduring quality of this anthology will be its flexibility. Select from the middle, the beginning or the end. Read only one piece or enjoy several selections at a sitting. Humor is personal; it is practically impossible to predict what will make an individual laugh. It is remarkable that such a young nation can offer the reader so marvelous an array of humor. The choices herein are so varied that all should find much to tickle their funny bones.

Benjamin Franklin
[1706–1790]

Generally regarded as the first American literary
humorist, Benjamin Franklin was known to his
contemporaries as a printer, publisher, inventor scientist, public servant, and statesman. Today Franklin is probably best remembered for
his identification of lightning with electricity,
for his widely read *Autobiography,* and for fur-
thering the welfare of the British colonies which
later became the United States of America.

Franklin's philosophy of honesty, industry,
and frugality permeates his writings, particularly
Poor Richard's Almanack, which he first published in 1732 and continued for twenty-five
years. This was a tremendously popular publication and was read by all classes in the colonies. *The Way to Wealth,* which appeared in
the final *Almanack,* draws together many of
Poor Richard's best-known sayings. As Franklin
himself explained: "These proverbs, which contained the wisdom of many ages and nations, I
assembled and form'd into a connected discourse prefix'd to the *Almanack* of 1757, as the
harangue of a wise old man to the people at-
tending an auction."

THE WAY TO WEALTH

Courteous Reader

I have heard that nothing gives an Author so great Pleasure, as to find his Works respectfully quoted by other learned Authors. This Pleasure I have seldom enjoyed; for tho' I have been, if I may say it without Vanity, an *eminent Author* of Almanacks annually now a full Quarter of a Century, my Brother Authors in the same Way, for what Reason I know not, have ever been very sparing in their Applauses, and no other Author has taken the least Notice of me, so that did not my Writings produce me some solid *Pudding*, the great Deficiency of *Praise* would have quite discouraged me.

I concluded at length, that the People were the best Judges of my Merit; for they buy my Works; and besides, in my Rambles, where I am not personally known, I have frequently heard one or other of my Adages repeated, with, *as Poor Richard says*, at the End on 't; this gave me some Satisfaction, as it showed not only that my Instructions were regarded, but discovered likewise some Respect for my Authority; and I own, that to encourage the Practice of remembering and repeating those wise Sentences, I have sometimes *quoted myself* with great Gravity.

Judge, then how much I must have been gratified by an Incident I am going to relate to you. I stopt my Horse lately where a great Number of People were collected at a Vendue of Merchant Goods. The Hour of Sale not being come, they were conversing on the Badness of the Times and one of the Company call'd to a plain clean old Man, with white Locks, "Pray, Father Abraham, what think you of the Times? Won't these heavy Taxes quite ruin the Country? How shall we be ever able to pay them? What would you advise us to?" Father *Abraham* stood up, and reply'd, "If you'd have my Advice, I'll give it you in short, for *A Word to the Wise is enough*, and *many Words won't fill a Bushel*, as *Poor Richard* says." They join'd in desiring him to speak his Mind, and gathering round him, he proceeded as follows:

"Friends," says he, and Neighbours, "the Taxes are indeed very heavy, and if those laid on by the Government were the only Ones we had to pay, we might more easily discharge them; but we have many others, and much more grievous to some of us. We are taxed twice as much by our *Idleness*, three times as much by our *Pride*, and four times as much by our *Folly*; and from these Taxes the Commissioners cannot ease or deliver us by allowing an Abatement. However let us hearken to good Advice, and something may be done for us; *God helps them that help themselves*, as *Poor Richard* says, in his Almanack of 1733.

"It would be thought a hard Government that should tax its People one-tenth Part of their *Time*, to be employed in its Service. But *Idleness* taxes many of us much more, if we reckon all that is spent in absolute *Sloth*, or doing of nothing, with that which is spent in idle Employments or Amusements, that amount to nothing. *Sloth*, by bringing on Diseases, absolutely shortens life. *Sloth, like Rust, consumes faster than Labour wears; while the used Key is always bright*, as *Poor Richard* says. *But dost thou love Life, then do not squander Time, for that's the stuff Life is made of*, as *Poor Richard* says. How much more than is necessary do we spend in sleep, forgetting that *The sleeping Fox catches no Poultry*, and that *There will be sleeping enough in the Grave*, as *Poor Richard* says.

"*If Time be of all Things the most precious, wasting Time must be*, as *Poor Richard* says, *the greatest*

Prodigality; since, as he elsewhere tells us, *Lost Time is never found again; and what we call Time enough, always proves little enough*: Let us then up and be doing, and doing to the Purpose; so by Diligence shall we do more with less Perplexity. *Sloth makes all Things difficult, but Industry all easy*, as Poor Richard says; and *He that riseth late must trot all Day, and shall scarce overtake his Business at Night*; while *Laziness travels so slowly, that Poverty soon overtakes him*, as we read in Poor Richard, who adds, *Drive thy Business, let not that drive thee*; and *Early to Bed, and early to rise, makes a Man healthy, wealthy, and wise*.

"So what signifies *wishing* and *hoping* for better Times. We may make these Times better, if we bestir ourselves. *Industry need not wish*, as Poor Richard says, *and he that lives upon Hope will die fasting. There are no Gains without Pains; then Help Hands, for I have no Lands*, or if I have, they are smartly taxed. And, as Poor Richard likewise observes, *He that hath a Trade hath an Estate; and he that hath a Calling, hath an Office of Profit and Honour*; but then the *Trade* must be worked at, and the *Calling* well followed, or neither the *Estate* nor the *Office* will enable us to pay our Taxes. If we are industrious, we shall never starve; for, as Poor Richard says, *At the working Man's House Hunger looks in, but dares not enter*. Nor will the Bailiff or the Constable enter, for *Industry pays Debts, while Despair encreaseth them*, says Poor Richard. What though you have found no Treasure, nor has any rich Relation left you a Legacy, *Diligence is the Mother of Good-luck* as Poor Richard says *and God gives all Things to Industry. Then plough deep, while Sluggards sleep, and you shall have Corn to sell and to keep*, says Poor Dick. Work while it is called To-day, for you know not how much you may be hindered To-morrow, which makes Poor Richard say, *One to-day is worth two To-morrows*, and farther, *Have you somewhat to do To-morrow, do it To-day*. If you were a Servant, would you not be ashamed that a good Master should catch you idle? Are you then your own Master, *be ashamed to catch yourself idle*, as *Poor Dick* says. When there is so much to be done for yourself, your Family, your Country, and your gracious King, be up by Peep of Day; *Let not the Sun look down and say, Inglorious here he lies*. Handle your Tools without Mittens; remember that *The Cat in Gloves catches no Mice*, as *Poor Richard* says. 'Tis true there is much to be done, and perhaps you are weak-handed, but stick to it steadily; and you will see great Effects, for *Constant Dropping wears away Stones*, and by *Diligence and Patience the Mouse ate in two the Cable*; and *Little Strokes fell great Oaks*, as *Poor Richard* says in his Almanack, the Year I cannot just now remember.

"Methinks I hear some of you say, *Must a Man afford himself no Leisure?* I will tell thee, my friend, what *Poor Richard* says, *Employ thy Time well, if thou meanest to gain Leisure; and, since thou art not sure of a Minute, throw not away an Hour*. Leisure, is Time for doing something useful; this Leisure the diligent Man will obtain, but the lazy Man never; so that, as *Poor Richard* says, *A Life of Leisure and a Life of Laziness are two Things*. Do you imagine that Sloth will afford you more Comfort than Labour? No, for as *Poor Richard* says, *Trouble springs from Idleness, and grievous Toil from needless Ease. Many without Labour, would live by their Wits only, but they break for want of Stock*. Whereas Industry gives Comfort, and Plenty, and Respect: *Fly Pleasures, and they'll follow you. The diligent Spinner has a large Shift; and now I have a Sheep and a Cow, every-Body bids me good Morrow*; all which is well said by *Poor Richard*.

"But with our Industry, we must likewise be *steady, settled*, and *careful*, and oversee our own Affairs *with our own Eyes*, and not trust too much to others; for, as *Poor Richard* says

"*I never saw an oft-removed Tree,*
    Nor yet an oft-removed Family,
    That throve so well as those that settled be.

And again, *Three Removes is as bad as a Fire*; and again, *Keep thy Shop, and thy Shop will keep thee*; and again, *If you would have your Business done, go; if not, send.* And again,

> "He that by the Plough would thrive,
>   Himself must either hold or drive.

And again, *The Eye of a Master will do more Work than both his Hands*; and again, *Want of Care does us more Damage than Want of Knowledge*; and again, *Not to oversee Workmen, is to leave them your Purse open.* Trusting too much to others' Care is the Ruin of many; for, as the Almanack says, *In the Affairs of this World, Men are saved, not by Faith, but by the Want of it*; but a Man's own Care is profitable; for, saith *Poor Dick, Learning is to the Studious, and Riches to the Careful*, as well as *Power to the Bold*, and *Heaven to the Virtuous.* And farther, *If you would have a faithful Servant, and one that you like, serve yourself.* And again, he adviseth to Circumspection and Care, even in the smallest Matters, because sometimes *A little Neglect may breed great Mischief*; adding, *for want of a Nail the Shoe was lost; for want of a Shoe the Horse was lost; and for want of a Horse the Rider was lost, being overtaken and slain by the Enemy; all for want of Care about a Horse-shoe Nail.*

"So much for Industry, my Friends, and Attention to one's own Business; but to these we must add *Frugality*, if we would make our *Industry* more certainly successful. A Man may, if he knows not how to save as he gets, *keep his Nose all his Life to the Grindstone*, and die not worth a *Groat* at last. *A fat Kitchen makes a lean Will*, as Poor Richard says; and

> "*Many Estates are spent in the Getting,*
>   *Since Women for Tea forsook Spinning and Knitting,*
>   *And Men for Punch forsook Hewing and Splitting.*

If you would be wealthy, says he, in another Almanack, *think of Saving as well as of Getting: The Indies have not made Spain rich, because her Outgoes are greater than her Incomes.*

"Away then with your expensive Follies, and you will not then have so much Cause to complain of hard Times, heavy Taxes, and chargeable Families; for, as *Poor Dick* says,

"*Women and Wine, Game and Deceit,*
Make the Wealth small and the Wants great.

And farther, *What maintains one Vice, would bring up two Children.* You may think perhaps, that a *little* Tea, or a *little* Punch now and then, Diet a *little* more costly, Clothes a *little* finer, and a *little* Entertainment now and then, can be no *great* Matter; but remember what *Poor Richard* says, *Many a Little makes a Mickle*; and farther, *Beware of little Expences; A small Leak will sink a great Ship*; and again, *Who Dainties love, shall Beggars prove*; and moreover, *Fools make Feasts, and wise Men eat them.*

"Here you are all got together at this Vendue of *Fineries* and *Knicknacks*. You call them *Goods*; but if you do not take Care, they will prove *Evils* to some of you. You expect they will be sold *cheap*, and perhaps they may for less than they cost; but if you have no Occasion for them, they must be *dear* to you. Remember what *Poor Richard* says; *Buy what thou hast no Need of, and ere long thou shalt sell thy Necessaries.* And again, *At a great Pennyworth pause a while*: He means, that perhaps the Cheapness is *apparent* only, and not *Real*; or the bargain, by straitening thee in thy Business, may do thee more Harm than Good. For in another Place he says, *Many have been ruined by buying good Pennyworths.* Again, *Poor Richard* says, 'tis *foolish to lay out Money in a Purchase of Repentance*; and yet this Folly is practised every Day at Vendues, for want of minding the Almanack. *Wise Men*, as *Poor Dick* says, *learn by others Harms, Fools scarcely*

*by their own; but felix quem faciunt aliena pericula
cautum.* Many a one, for the Sake of Finery on the
Back, have gone with a hungry Belly, and half-starved
their Families. *Silks and Sattins, Scarlet and Velvets,*
as *Poor Richard* says, *put out the Kitchen Fire.*

"These are not the *Necessaries* of Life; they can
scarcely be called the *Conveniences;* and yet only
because they look pretty, how many *want* to *have*
them! The *artificial* Wants of Mankind thus become
more numerous than the *Natural;* and, as *Poor Dick*
says, *for one poor Person, there are an hundred indigent.*
By these, and other Extravagancies, the Genteel are
reduced to poverty, and forced to borrow of those
whom they formerly despised, but who through Industry and Frugality have maintained their Standing;
in which Case it appears plainly, that *A Ploughman
on his Legs is higher than a Gentleman on his Knees,*
as *Poor Richard* says. Perhaps they have had a small
Estate left them, which they knew not the Getting of;
they think, *'tis Day, and will never be Night;* that a
little to be spent out of *so much,* is not worth minding.
A Child and a Fool, as *Poor Richard* says, *imagine
Twenty shillings and Twenty Years can never be spent*
but, *always taking out of the Meal-tub, and never
putting in, soon comes to the Bottom;* as *Poor Dick*
says, *When the Well's dry, they know the Worth of
Water.* But this they might have known before, if they
had taken his Advice: *If you would know the Value of
Money, go and try to borrow some; for, he that goes a
borrowing goes a sorrowing;* and indeed so does he that
lends to such People, when he goes *to get it in again.*
Poor Dick farther advises, and says,

> "Fond Pride of Dress is sure a very Curse;
> E'er Fancy you consult, consult your Purse.

And again, *Pride is as loud a Beggar as Want, and a
great deal more saucy.* When you have bought one fine
Thing, you must buy ten more, that your Appearance

may be all of a Piece; but *Poor Dick* says, *'Tis easier to suppress the first Desire, than to satisfy all that follow it.* And 'tis as truly Folly for the Poor to ape the Rich, as for the Frog to swell, in order to equal the ox.

> "*Great Estates may venture more,*
> *But little Boats should keep near Shore.*

'Tis, however, a Folly soon punished; for *Pride that dines on Vanity, sups on Contempt,* as Poor Richard says. And in another Place, *Pride breakfasted with Plenty, dined with Poverty, and supped with Infamy.* And after all, of what Use is this *Pride of Appearance,* for which so much is risked, so much is suffered? It cannot promote Health, or ease Pain; it makes no Increase of Merit in the Person, it creates Envy, it hastens Misfortune.

> "*What is a Butterfly? At best*
> *He's but a Caterpillar drest*
> *The gaudy Fop's his Picture just,*

as *Poor Richard* says.

"But what Madness must it be to *run in Debt* for these Superfluities! We are offered, by the Terms of this Vendue, *Six Months' Credit;* and that perhaps has induced some of us to attend it, because we cannot spare the ready Money, and hope now to be fine without it. But, ah, think what you do when you run in Debt; *you give to another Power over your Liberty.* If you cannot pay at the Time, you will be ashamed to see your Creditor; you will be in Fear when you speak to him; you will make poor pitiful sneaking Excuses, and by Degrees come to lose your Veracity, and sink into base downright lying; for, as *Poor Richard* says, *The second Vice is Lying, the first is running in Debt.* And again, to the same Purpose, *Lying rides upon Debt's back.* Whereas a free-born *Englishman* ought not to be ashamed or afraid to see or speak to any Man living. But Poverty often deprives a Man of all Spirit and

Virtue: *'Tis hard for an empty Bag to stand upright*, as *Poor Richard* truly says.

"What would you think of that Prince, or that Government, who should issue an Edict forbidding you to dress like a Gentleman or a Gentlewoman, on Pain of Imprisonment or Servitude? Would you not say, that you were free, have a Right to dress as you please, and that such an Edict would be a Breach of your Privileges, and such a Government tyrannical? And yet you are about to put yourself under that Tyranny, when you run in Debt for such Dress! Your Creditor has Authority, at his Pleasure to deprive you of your Liberty, by confining you in Gaol for Life, or to sell you for a Servant, if you should not be able to pay him! When you have got your Bargain, you may, perhaps, think little of Payment; but *Creditors, Poor Richard* tells us, *have better Memories than Debtors*; and in another Place says, *Creditors are a superstitious Sect, great Observers of set Days and Times*. The Day comes round before you are aware, and the Demand is made before you are prepared to satisfy it, or if you bear your Debt in Mind, the Term 'which at first seemed so long, will, as it lessens, appear extreamly short. *Time* will seem to have added Wings to his Heels as well as Shoulders. *Those have a short Lent,* saith *Poor Richard, who owe Money to be paid at Easter*. Then since, as he says, *The Borrower is a Slave to the Lender, and the Debtor to the Creditor*, disdain the Chain, preserve your Freedom; and maintain your Independency: Be *industrious* and *free*; be *frugal* and *free*. At present, perhaps, you may think yourself in thriving Circumstances, and that you can bear a little Extravagance without Injury; but,

> "For Age and Want, save while you may;
> No Morning Sun lasts a whole day,

as *Poor Richard* says. Gain may be temporary and uncertain, but ever while you live, Expence is constant and certain; and *'tis easier to build two Chimnies, than to keep one in Fuel*, as Poor Richard says. So, *Rather go to Bed supperless than rise in Debt.*

> "*Get what you can, and what you get hold;*
> *'Tis the Stone that will turn all your lead into Gold,*

as *Poor Richard* says. And when you have got the Philosopher's Stone, sure you will no longer complain of bad Times, or the Difficulty of paying Taxes.

"This Doctrine, my Friends, is *Reason* and *Wisdom*; but after all, do not depend too much upon your own *Industry*, and *Frugality*, and *Prudence*, though excellent Things, for they may all be blasted without the Blessing of Heaven; and therefore, ask that Blessing humbly, and be not uncharitable to those that at present seem to want it, but comfort and help them. Remember, *Job* suffered, and was afterwards prosperous.

"And now to conclude, *Experience keeps a dear School, but Fools will learn in no other, and scarce in that*; for it is true, *we may give Advice, but we cannot give Conduct*, as Poor Richard says: However, remember this, *They that won't be counselled, can't be helped*, as *Poor Richard* says: and farther, That, *if you will not hear Reason, she'll surely rap your knuckles.*"

Thus the old Gentleman ended his Harangue. The People heard it, and approved the Doctrine, and immediately practised the contrary, just as if it had been a common Sermon; for the Vendue opened, and they began to buy extravagantly, notwithstanding, his Cautions and their own Fear of Taxes. I found the good Man had thoroughly studied my Almanacks, and digested all I had dropt on these Topicks during the Course of Five and twenty Years. The frequent Mention he made of me must have tired any one else, but my Vanity was wonderfully delighted with it, though I was conscious that not a tenth Part of the Wisdom was my own, which he ascribed to me, but rather the *Gleanings* I had made of the Sense of all Ages and

Nations. However, I resolved to be the better for the Echo of it; and though I had at first determined to buy Stuff for a new Coat, I went away resolved to wear my old One a little longer. *Reader*, if thou wilt do the same, thy Profit will be as great as mine. I *am, as ever, thine to serve thee,*

RICHARD SAUNDERS
July 7, 1757

David (Davy) Crockett
[1786–1836]

David (Davy) Crockett, the American frontiers-
man who became a legend in his own time,
was born in a pioneer cabin in Eastern Tennessee. His formal education consisted of 100 days
of tutoring by a neighbor. He served with distinction in the militia under Andrew Jackson,
and in 1821 was elected to the Tennessee legislature, winning popularity through his cam-
paign speeches filled with homespun yarns. He
later served three terms in Congress, where
his backwoods bravado and gift of gab thrust
him into the role of frontier folk hero—a role
he relished and played to the hilt. He was de-
feated for reelection in 1835 and died in Texas
the following year in the defense of the Alamo.
This excerpt from his autobiography is typical
of his flamboyant manner and devil-may-care
outlook. Some of the writings attributed to
Crockett may have been ghostwritten, but they
are characteristic in every respect.

THE COON-SKIN TRICK

While on the subject of election matters, I will just relate a little anecdote about myself, which will show the people to the East how we manage these things on the frontiers. It was when I first run for Congress; I was then in favor of the Hero [Andrew Jackson], for he had chalked out his course so sleek in his letter to the Tennessee legislature that, like Sam Patch, says I, "There can be no mistake in him," and so I went ahead. No one dreamt about the monster and the deposits at that time, and so, as I afterward found, many like myself were taken in by these fair promises, which were worth about as much as a flash in the pan when you have a fair shot at a fat bear.

But I am losing sight of my story. Well, I started off to the Cross Roads dressed in my hunting shirt, and my rifle on my shoulder. Many of our constituents had assembled there to get a taste of the quality of the candidates at orating. Job Snelling, a gander-shanked Yankee, who had been caught somewhere about Plymouth Bay, and been shipped to the West with a cargo of codfish and rum, erected a large shantee, and set up shop for the occasion. A large posse of the voters had assembled before I arrived, and my opponent had already made considerable headway with his speechifying and his treating, when they spied me about a rifle shot from camp, sauntering along as if I was not a party in business. "There comes Crockett," cried one. "Let us hear the colonel," cried another; and so I mounted the stump that had been cut down for the occasion, and began to bushwhack in the most approved style.

I had not been up long before there was such an uproar in the crowd that I could not hear my own voice, and some of my constituents let me know that they could not listen to me on such a dry subject as the welfare of the nation until they had something to drink, and that I must treat them. Accordingly I jumped down from the rostrum, and led the way to the shantee, followed by my constituents, shouting, "Huzza for Crockett!" and "Crockett forever!"

When we entered the shantee Job was busy dealing out his rum in a style that showed he was making a good day's work of it, and I called for a quart of the best; but the crooked crittur returned no other answer than by pointing to a board over the bar, on which he had chalked in large letters, *"Pay to-day and trust to-morrow."* Now that idea brought me up all standing; it was a sort of cornering in which there was no back-out, for ready money in the West, in those times, was the shyest thing in all nature, and it was most particularly shy with me on that occasion.

The voters, seeing my predicament, fell off to the other side, and I was left deserted and alone, as the Government will be, when he no longer has any offices to bestow. I saw as plain as day that the tide of popular opinion was against me, and that unless I got some rum speedily I should lose my election as sure as there are snakes in Virginny; and it must be done soon, or even burnt brandy wouldn't save me. So I walked away from the shantee, but in another guess sort from the way I entered it, for on this occasion I had no train after me, and not a voice shouted, "Huzza for Crockett!" Popularity sometimes depends on a very small matter indeed; in this particular it was worth a quart of New England rum, and no more.

Well, knowing that a crisis was at hand, I struck into the woods, with my rifle on my shoulder, my best friend in time of need; and, as good fortune would have it, I had not been out more than a quarter of an hour before I treed a fat coon, and in the pulling of a trigger he lay dead at the foot of the tree. I soon whipped his hairy jacket off his back, and again bent my steps towards the shantee, and walked up to the bar, but not alone, for this time I had half a dozen of my constituents at my heels. I threw down the coon-skin upon the counter, and called for a quart, and Job, though busy dealing out rum, forgot to point at his chalked rules and regulations; for he knew that a coon was as good a legal tender for a quart in the West as a New York shilling any day in the year.

My constituents now flocked about me, and cried, "Huzza for Crockett!" "Crockett forever!" and finding the tide had taken a turn, I told them several yarns to get them in a good humor; and having soon dispatched the value of the coon, I went out and mounted the stump without opposition, and a clear majority of the voters followed me to hear what I had to offer for the good of the nation. Before I was half through one of my constituents moved that they would hear the balance of my speech after they had washed down the first part with some more of Job Snelling's extract of cornstalk and molasses, and the question being put, it was carried unanimously. It wasn't considered necessary to tell the yeas and nays, so we adjourned to the shantee, and on the way I began to reckon that the fate of the nation pretty much depended upon my shooting another coon.

While standing at the bar, feeling sort of bashful while Job's rules and regulations stared me in the face, I cast down my eyes, and discovered one end of the coon-skin sticking between the logs that supported the bar. Job had slung it there in the hurry of business. I gave it a sort of quick jerk, and it followed my hand as natural as if I had been the rightful owner. I slapped it on the counter, and Job, little dreaming that he was barking up the wrong tree, shoved along another bottle, which my constituents quickly disposed of with great good humor, for some of them saw the trick; and then we withdrew to the rostrum to discuss the affairs of the nation.

I don't know how it was, but the voters soon became dry again, and nothing would do but we must adjourn to the shantee; and as luck would have it, the coon-skin was still sticking between the logs, as if Job had flung it there on purpose to tempt me. I was not slow in raising it to the counter, the rum followed, of course, and I wish I may be shot if I didn't, before the day was over, get ten quarts for the same identical skin, and from a fellow, too, who in those parts was considered as sharp as a steel trap and as bright as a pewter button.

This joke secured me my election, for it soon circulated like smoke among my constituents, and they allowed, with one accord, that the man who could get the whip hand of Job Snelling in fair trade, could outwit Old Nick himself, and was the real grit for them in Congress. Job was by no means popular; he boasted of always being wide awake, and that any one who could take him in was free to do so, for he came from a stock that, sleeping or waking, had always one eye open, and the other not more than half closed. The whole family were geniuses. His father was the inventor of wooden nutmegs, by which Job said he might have made a fortune, if he had only taken out a patent and kept the business in his own hands; his mother, Patience, manufactured the first white oak pumpkin seeds of the mammoth kind, and turned a pretty penny the first season; and his aunt Prudence was the first to discover that corn husks, steeped into tobacco water, would make as handsome Spanish wrappers as ever came from Havana, and that oak leaves would answer all the purpose of filling, for no one could discover the difference except the man who smoked them, and then it would be too late to make a stir about it. Job himself bragged of having made some useful discoveries, the most profitable of which was the art of converting mahogany sawdust into cayenne pepper, which he said was a profitable and safe business; for the people have been so long accustomed to having dust thrown in their eyes that there wasn't much danger of being found out.

The way I got to the blind side of the Yankee merchant was pretty generally known before election day, and the result was that my opponent might as well have whistled jigs to a milestone as attempt to beat up for votes in that district. I beat him out and out, quite back into the old year, and there was scarce enough left of him, after the canvass was over, to make a small grease spot. He disappeared without even leaving a mark behind; and such will be the fate of Adam Huntsman, if there is a fair fight and no gouging.

After the election was over, I sent Snelling the price of the rum, but took good care to keep the fact from the knowledge of my constituents. Job refused the money, and sent me word that it did him good to be taken in occasionally, as it served to brighten his ideas; but I afterwards learnt when he found out the trick that had been played upon him, he put all the rum I had ordered in his bill against my opponent, who, being elated with the speeches he had made on the affairs of the nation, could not descend to examine into the particulars of a bill of a vender of rum in the small way.

Oliver Wendell Holmes
[1809–1894]

Oliver Wendell Holmes, the urbane New England wit, excelled in both branches of his dual career in literature and medicine. Born and reared in Cambridge, Massachusetts, he attended Harvard University, first as an undergraduate, and later as a graduate student in law and medicine. As professor of anatomy and physiology at Harvard Medical School, Holmes distinguished himself as a lively and informative lecturer. He published important scientific papers that spurred medical reform. Yet Holmes is even better known as a man of letters. His light verse, essays and novels blend humor and pathos in their treatment of historical events, public affairs, and religious issues. A stimulating and charming conversationalist, he led the renowned Boston literary group, the Saturday Club. His contributions to *The Atlantic Monthly* (which he named) were considered responsible for that magazine's early success. These informal sketches were later collected in the enormously popular *Autocrat of the Breakfast Table*. When Holmes visited England at the age of seventy-seven, his resounding reception confirmed his international reputation.

THE BALLAD OF THE OYSTERMAN

It was a tall young oysterman lived by the river-side,
His shop was just upon the bank, his boat was on the
tide;
The daughter of a fisherman, that was so straight and
slim,
Lived over on the other bank, right opposite to him.

It was the pensive oysterman that saw a lovely maid, 5
Upon a moonlight evening, a-sitting in the shade:
He saw her wave her handkerchief, as much as if to say,
"I'm wide awake, young oysterman, and all the folks
away."

Then up arose the oysterman, and to himself said he,
"I guess I'll leave the skiff at home, for fear that folks
should see; 10
I read it in the story-book, that, for to kiss his dear,
Leander swam the Hellespont, —and I will swim this
here."

And he has leaped into the waves, and crossed the
shining stream,
And he has clambered up the bank, all in the moonlight
gleam;
Oh there were kisses sweet as dew, and words as soft as
rain,— 15
But they have heard her father's step, and in he leaps
again!

Out spoke the ancient fisherman, —"Oh, what was that, my daughter?"

"'Twas nothing but a pebble, sir, I threw into the water."

"And what is that, pray tell me, love, that paddles off so fast?"

"It's nothing but a porpoise, sir, that's been a-swimming past." 20

Out spoke the ancient fisherman, —"Now bring me my harpoon!

I'll get into my fishing-boat, and fix the fellow soon."

Down fell that pretty innocent, as falls a snow-white lamb,

Her hair drooped round her pallid cheeks, like seaweed on a clam.

Alas for those two loving ones! she waked not from her swound, 25

And he was taken with the cramp, and in the waves was drowned;

But Fate has metamorphosed them, in pity of their woe,

And now they keep an oyster-shop for mermaids down below.

MY AUNT

My aunt! my dear unmarried aunt!
  Long years have o'er her flown;
Yet still she strains the aching clasp
  That binds her virgin zone;
I know it hurts her, —though she looks   5
  As cheerful as she can;
Her waist is ampler than her life,
  For life is but a span.

My aunt! my poor deluded aunt!
  Her hair is almost gray;   10
Why will she train that winter curl
  In such a spring-like way?
How can she lay her glasses down,
  And say she reads as well,
When through a double convex lens   15
  She just makes out to spell?

Her father—grandpapa! forgive
  This erring lip its smiles—
Vowed she should make the finest girl
  Within a hundred miles;   20
He sent her to a stylish school;
  'Twas in her thirteenth June;
And with her, as the rules required,
  "Two towels and a spoon."

They braced my aunt against a board,   25
  To make her straight and tall;

They laced her up, they starved her down,
   To make her light and small;
They pinched her feet, they singed her hair,
   They screwed it up with pins;—   30
Oh, never mortal suffered more
   In penance for her sins.

So, when my precious aunt was done,
   My grandsire brought her back
(By daylight, lest some rabid youth   35
   Might follow on the track);
"Ah!" said my grandsire, as he shook
   Some powder in his pan,
"What could this lovely creature do
   Against a desperate man!"   40

Alas! nor chariot, nor barouche,
   Nor bandit cavalcade,
Tore from the trembling father's arms
   His all-accomplished maid.
For her how happy had it been!
   And Heaven had spared to me
To see one sad, ungathered rose
   On my ancestral tree.

Josh Billings
[1818–1885]

"Josh Billings" was born Henry Wheeler Shaw, the descendant of New England stock. He suffered through a year of college and adventured in the West, working at a wide variety of odd jobs before settling down in Poughkeepsie, New York, as an auctioneer and land dealer. He began to write relatively late in life, but rapidly became successful as a writer and lecturer, reaching national fame after 1867, when he joined the *New York Weekly* as an "exclusive" contributor. Under the name of Josh Billings, he enjoyed tremendous popularity with his sketches, "letters," and annual Allminax. In the selections included here, he appears as "Uncle Josh," the gruff, cracker-barrel humorist and philosopher, standing up for common sense, fair play, and the values of the "good old days."

UNCLE JOSH BIDS YOU
A FOND ADIEU

I have got grandchildren and they are worse than the first crop to riot among the feelings.

The grandpa is an individual, aged somewhere between fifty and one hundred years, of a promiscuous temperament, and is a common occurrence in all well-regulated families. Next to a healthy mother-in-law, they have more active business on hand than any other party in the household.

They are the standard authority on all leading topics, and what they don't know about things that took place sixty-five years ago, or will take place for the next sixty-five years to come, is a damage for anyone to know.

Grandpas are not entirely useless. They are handy to hold babies and feed the pigs and are very smart at mending a broken broom handle, sifting coal ashes, and putting clothes on the line on washdays.

I have seen grandpas that could churn good, but I consider it a mighty mean trick to set an old fellow of eighty years to churning butter. I am a grandpa myself, but I won't churn butter for no concern, not if I understand myself. I am as solid on this conclusion as a graven image. I am willing to rock baby all the time while the womenfolks are boiling soap; I am willing to cut rags, to work up into rag carpets; they can keep me hunting hens' eggs wet days or picking green currants; I will even dip candles or core apples for sauce or turn a grindstone; but, by thunder, I won't churn. I have examined myself on this subject and I will be a

jackknife, so long as he remains in his right mind,
Josh Billings won't churn.

As a general thing grandpas are a set of conceited
old fools who don't seem to realize that what they
know themselves is the result of experience and that
younger people have got to get their knowledge the
same way. Grandpas are poor help at bringing up
children; they have got precept and catechism enough,
but the young ones all seem to understand that
Grandpa minds them a heap more than they mind
Grandpa.

*Like most grandpas he also looked with nostalgia at
the days of yore—the good old days:*

In ancient days, men, after considering an enterprise,
proceeded with energy to execute it; now they shut up
one eye and "pitch in."

In old times, if their judgment sanctioned, they
considered the chances; now, they "let her rip."

Then, they drank moderately of water and brandy;
now, they smile aqua fortis and suck sweet-scented
turpentine through a quill.

Then, if circumstances made it imperative, they
closed their business by effecting an honorable compromise; now, they "cave in," "squeal," or "absquat."

Then, contrary opinions were occasionally supported
with reasonable wagers; now, every man "bets his pile"
or "bottom dollar."

Then, most families held from six to ten healthy
children, within its hallowed circle a radiant mother,
and a stalwart sire; now, too often a puny father with
uncertain knees, a romantic madam with a pale lily
at her breast, a wet nurse, two Bridgets and a kennel
of sore-eyed pups.

Then, they went to meeting, to hear a doctrine
sermon, and be humble before God; now, they flaunt
into holy palaces and pay out fortunes every year to
lounge on velvet and hear the Bible amateured by a
dainty gentleman who handles their sins as he would
a sleeping infant.

Then, our halls of legislature were filled with honest patriots; now, with clever bandits, whose courtesies dwell upon the tips of Bowie knives and whose eloquence and arguments are resting in the chambers of deadly revolvers.

Then, we had youths apprenticed to an honest calling, whose indentures were diplomas; now, pale young gentlemen, emulous of physic or the law, who are pendant to the purlieus of the courts and colleges, watching for the falling of a crumb.

Then, we had maidens until they had been looked upon by at least twenty summers and were modest enough to pick out a husband from a score of earnest and honest men, whose very eyes had the promise of bread in them; now, fifteen summers make a woman (or what we are obliged to take for one) and one so ripe, too, that he who first shakes the bush, gets the eager fruit.

Then our literature and learning was drawn from sound philosophy or quaint proverbs of sense, and the few books that prevailed were good; now, everybody writes a book, and every fool reads it; learning is stereotyped and wisdom is only twelve shillings a volume.

Then, industry created wants, virtue tempered them, and frugality supplied them; now, luxury has taken the place of industry, pride the place of virtue, and extravagance the place of frugality.

Then, men were solicitous about their characters; now, about their pedigrees.

Then, they found health at home; now, they hunt for it by travel.

Finally—if our grandpops should come among us with the plans and precepts of a hundred years ago, we, in our impudence and wickedness, would be caught laughing at them, while they, in virtuous sorrow, would be in tears over us, and thus would be enacted the scenes which always ensue when fools and sages meet.

How I do long (once in a while) for them good old

days. Them days when the sun didn't rise before break-fast. Them days when there was more fun in thirty cents than there is now in seven dollars and a half. Them days when a man married 145 pounds of woman and less than nine pounds (all told) of anything else.

How I long for them good old days when education consisted in what a man did well. Them days when deacons was as austere as horse-radish and ministers preached to men's souls instead of their pockets. Them days when politics was the exception and honesty the rule.

How I do long for them good old days when lap dogs and wet nurses warn't known, and when brown bread and baked goose made a good dinner. Them days when a man who wasn't busy was watched, and when women spun only that kind of yarn that was good for darning of stockings.

How I do long for them good old days when now and then a gal baby was named Jerusha, and a boy wasn't spoilt if he was named Jeremiah.

All you who have tried the feathers and fuss of life, who have had the codfish of wealth, without sense, stuck under your nose, must long with me for them good old days when men were ashamed to be fools and women were ashamed to be flirts.

N.B. They used to make a milk punch in them days too, that was very handy to take.

FROM
<u>UNCLE JOSH'S ZOO</u>

The Ant

The ant has no holidays, no eight-hour system, nor never strikes for higher wages. They are cheerful little toilers and have no malice nor back door to their hearts. There is no sedentary loafers among them and you never see one out of a job. They get up early, go to bed late, work all the time, and eat on the run.

You never see two ants arguing some foolish question that neither of them don't understand; they don't care whether the moon is inhabited or not; nor whether a fish weighing two pounds put into a pail of water already full will make the pail slop over or weigh more. They ain't hunting after the philosopher's stone or getting crazy over the cause of the sudden earthquake. They don't care whether Jupiter is thirty or thirty-one millions of miles up in the air nor whether the earth bobs around on its axis or not, so long as it don't bob over their corncrib and spill their barley.

They are simple, little, busy ants, full of faith, working hard, living prudently, committing no sin, praising God by minding their own business, and dying when their time comes, to make room for the next crop of ants.

They are a reproach to the lazy, an encouragement to the industrious, a rebuke to the vicious, and a study to the Christian.

Ants have by-laws and a constitution and they mean something. Their laws ain't like our laws, made with a hole in them so that a man can steal a horse and ride through them on a walk. They don't have any legislators that you can buy, nor any judges, lying around on the half-shell, ready to be swallowed.

I rather like the ants and think now I shall sell out my money and real estate and join them.

Bed Bugs

I never saw anybody yet but what despised bed bugs. They are the meanest of all crawling, creeping, hopping or biting things. They dassent tackle a man by daylight but sneak in, after dark, and chaw him while he is fast asleep.

A mosquito will fight you in broad daylight, at short range, and give you a chance to knock in his sides; the flea is a game bug and will make a dash at you even in Broadway, but the bed bug is a garroter who waits till you strip and then picks out a mellow place to eat you.

Bed bugs are uncommon smart in a *small* way: one pair of them will stock a hair mattress in two weeks with bugs enough to last a small family a whole year.

Bed bugs when they have grown all they intend to are about the size of a bluejay's eye and have a brown complexion. When they start out to garrote they are as thin as a grease spot and when they get through garroting they are swelled up like a blister. It takes them three days to get the swelling out of them.

If bed bugs have any destiny to fill it must be their stomachs, but it seems to me that they must have been made by accident, just like slivers, just to stick into somebody. If they was got up for some wise purpose, they must have took the wrong road, for there can't be any wisdom in chawing a man all night long, and raising a family, besides, to follow the same trade. If there is some wisdom in this, I hope the bed bugs will chaw the folks who can see it, and leave me be because I am one of the heretics.

Flies tickle me but don't make me swear. It takes bed bugs at the hollow of night, a mean, loafing bed bug who steals out of a crack in the wall as silently as the sweat on a dog's nose, and then creeps as soft as a shadow on to the tenderest spot and begins to bore for my oil—it takes one of these foul fiends of blood and midnight to make me swear a word of two syllables.

The Cockroach

The cockroach is a bug at large. His is one of the luxuries of civilization. There is no mistaking the fact that he is one of a numerous family and that his attachment to the home of his boyhood speaks louder than thunder for his affectionate and unadulterated nature. He don't leave the place he was born at upon the slightest provocation, like the giddy and vagrant flea, until death (or some vile powder) knocks at his front door. He and his brothers and sisters may be seen with the naked eye, ever and anon, calmly climbing the white sugar bowl or running foot races between the butter plates.

The cockroach is born on the first of May and the first of November, and is ready for use in 15 days from date. They are born from an egg, four from each egg, and consequently they are all of them quadruplets. The maternal bug don't set upon the eggs but leaves them lie around loose, like a pint of spilt mustard seed, and don't seem to care a darn whether they get ripe or not. But I never knew a cockroach egg fail to put in an appearance. They are as sure to hatch out and run as Canada thistles or a bad cold.

The cockroach is of two colors, sorrel and black. They are always on the move. Their food seems to consist not so much in what they eat as what they travel and, often finding them dead in my soup at the boarding-house, I have come to the conclusion that they can't swim but they can float.

Every man has a right to pick his playmates but as for me I had rather visit knee deep among cockroaches than to hear the dying embers of a single mosquito's son or to know that there was just one bed bug left in the world and was waiting for my candle to go out and for me to pitch into bed.

N.B. To get rid of cockroaches—sell your house and lot, and flee to the mountains.

The Flea

The smallest animal of the brute creation and the most pesky is the flea. They are about the bigness of an onion seed and shine like a brand-new shot. They spring from low places and can spring further and faster than any of the bug-brutes. They bite worse than the mosquito for they bite on a run. One flea will go all over a man's suburbs in two minutes and leave him as freckled as the measles.

It is impossible to do anything well with a flea on you except swear, and fleas ain't afraid of that. The only way is to quit business of all kinds and hunt for the flea, and when you have found him, he ain't there. This is one of the flea mysteries—the faculty they have of being entirely lost just as soon as you have found them.

I don't suppose there is ever killed, on an average during any one year, more than sixteen fleas in the whole United States of America, unless there is a casualty of some kind. Once in a while there is a dog gets drowned sudden and then there may be a few fleas lost.

They are about as hard to kill as flaxseed is and if you don't mash them up as fine as ground pepper they will start business again, on a smaller capital, just as pestiferous as ever.

The Fly

The fly is a domestic but friendly insect, without brains and without guile, that make their appearance among mankind a good deal as the wind does, "where it listeth."

They are so universal at times that I have thought they didn't wait to be born, but took the first good chance that was offered and come just as they are.

They are said to be male and female, but I don't think they consider the marriage tie binding, for they look so much alike that it would be a great waste of time finding out which was who, and this would lead to never-ending fights—which is the rhubarb of domestic life.

They make their annual visit about the first of May (more or less depending on where you live) but don't get to buzzing good till the center of August. They stay with us until cold weather puts in and leave pretty much as they come.

Many of them are cut off in the flower of their youth, and usefulness, but this don't interfere with their census, for there is another steps right into their place and heirs their property.

Some lose their lives by lighting too near the rim of a toad's nose, and fall in, when the toad gapes, and others get badly stuck by fooling with molasses. Some visit the spiders and are induced to stay.

The fly is no respecter of persons. He lights onto the pouting lips of a sleeping loafer just as easy as he does onto the bosom of the queen of beauty, and will buzz an alderman or a hod carrier if they get in his way.

Flies, morally considered, are like a large share of the rest of human folks—they won't settle on a good healthy spot in a man, not if they can find a spot that is a little raw.

Their principal food is anything. They will pitch into a dead snake, or a quarter of beef, with the same anxiety, and will eat from sunrise till seven o'clock in the evening without getting more than half full.

The fly has a remarkable impoverished memory. You may drive him out of your ear and he will land on your forehead; hit him angrily and he will enter your nose; the oftener you get rid of him in one spot, the more he gets onto another; the only way to inculcate your meaning is to smash him up fine.

Although they hang around saloons a good deal, I never saw a fly the worse for liquor, but I have often seen liquor the worse for flies.

Flies see a great deal of society. They are admitted into all circles and if they remember one half that they see and hear, what a world of funny secrets would unfold! But flies are perfectly honorable and never betray a confidence.

What would some lovers give if they could only get a fly to blab—but a fly is a perfect gentleman. He eats off your plate, enjoys your conversation, sees sights and has more fun, and privileges, than a prime minister, or a dressing maid, but when you come to pump him, he is as dry in the mouth as a salt codfish.

There are some things a fly will blow, but they won't blow a secret.

I don't know of a more happy, whole-souled, honest critter, among the bug persuasion, than a handsome, square-built fly, taking a free ride in Central Park, with the Mayor and his wife, or a free lunch at Delmonico's with the minister from England, and then finishing up the business of the day by sleeping upside down on the ceiling of my lady's bedchamber.

I don't love a fly enough to leave my vittles and fall down flat on my stomach and worship him, but a fly may come and sit on my nose all day and chaw his cud in silence—if he will only sit still.

Louse

It is not the most delightful task to write the natural history of the louse. There is any quantity of thorough-bred folks who would consider it a contamination, as black as patent leather, to say louse or even think louse, but a louse is a fact, and all facts are never more at home, nor more unwilling to move, than when they get into the head.

The louse is one of the gems of antiquity. They are worn in the hair and are more ornamental than useful.

Not having any encyclopedia from which to sponge my information, and then pass it off for my own creation, I shall be forced, while talking about the louse, "to fight it out on the line" of observation, and when my knowledge, and experience, gives out, I shall tap my imagination of which I have a crude supply.

The louse is a familiar animal, very sedentary in his habits, not apt to get lost. They can be cultivated without the aid of a guidebook, and with half a chance will multiply and thicken as much as pimples on the goose.

The louse are well enough in their place, and for the sake of variety, perhaps a few of them are just as good as more would be.

In many ways the louse was our great stimulator in school. There is no ground so fruitful for the full development of this little domestic collateral as a district schoolhouse. While the young idea is breaking its shell and playing hide-and-go-seek on the inside of the dear urchin's skull, the louse is playing tag on the outside—and quite often gets on the schoolmarm.

I have always had a high veneration for the louse, not because I consider them as any evidence of genius, or even neatness, but because they remind me of my boyhood innocence, the days back in the alphabet of memory, when I sat on the flat side of a slab bench and spelt out old Webster with one hand, and stirred the top of my head with the other.

When, in the lapse of time, it comes to be revealed to us, that a single louse, chewing away on the summit of Daniel Webster's head, when he was a little schoolboy, was the telegraphic touch to the wire that bust the first idea in his brain, we shall see the wisdom of the louse, and shan't stick up our nose, until we turn a back somerset, at these venerable soldiers in the grand army of progression.

After we have reached years of discretion, and have got our education, and our characters have got done developing, and we begin to hold office, and are elected Justice of the Peace, for instance, and don't seem to need any more louse to stir us up, it is time enough to be sassy to them.

As for me, there is only one piece (thus far) of vital creation, that I actually *hate*, and that is a bed bug. I simply *despise* snakes, *fear* mosquitoes, *avoid* fleas, don't *associate* with the cockroach, go *around* toads, *back out square* for a hornet.

Nevertheless, moreover, to wit, I must say, even at this day of refinement, and belle lettres, I do actually love to stand on tiptoe and see a romping, red-cheeked, blue-eyed boy, chased up stairs and then out in the garden, and finally caught and throwed, and held firmly between his mother's knees, and see an old, warped, fine-toothed horn comb go and come, half buried through a flood of lawless hair, and drag each trip to the light, a fat and lively louse—and, in conclusion, to hear him pop as mother pins him with her thumbnail fast to the center of the comb. This fills me chuck up to the brim with something, I don't know what the feeling is, perhaps somebody out of a job can tell me.

Mark Twain
[1835–1910]

Robust frontier humor came to fruition in the works of Mark Twain. His genius for comic exaggeration, his gift of simple, strong narrative, and his unerring ear for American speech produced a distinctively American humor that made him famous worldwide. Samuel Langhorne Clemens grew up in Hannibal, Missouri, on the banks of the Mississippi River. He had little formal education and was apprenticed to a printer while still in his early teens. His sense of adventure led him to become a riverboat pilot on the Mississippi, and much of his literary material is drawn from his boyhood and his years on the river, including his best-known novels *The Adventures of Tom Sawyer* and *The Adventures of Huckleberry Finn*. When the Civil War interrupted river traffic, Clemens journeyed further west to Nevada and California and began writing for newspapers under the name Mark Twain. Publication of his short story "The Celebrated Jumping Frog of Calaveras County" first brought him to national attention. His prolific literary output and immensely popular public readings and lecture tours insured the growth of his reputation both here and abroad. In 1870 he married the genteel Olivia Langdon and settled down in Hartford, Connecticut to be "respectable," but continued to write novels, travel books, biographical works, humorous pieces, and journalism throughout his lifetime.

BUCK FANSHAW'S FUNERAL

Somebody has said that in order to know a community, one must observe the style of its funerals and know what manner of men they bury with most ceremony. I cannot say which class we buried with most éclat in our "flush times," the distinguished public benefactor or the distinguished rough—possibly the two chief grades or grand divisions of society honored their illustrious dead about equally; and hence, no doubt, the philosopher I have quoted from would have needed to see two representative funerals in Virginia before forming his estimate of the people.

There was a grand time over Buck Fanshaw when he died. He was a representative citizen. He had "killed his man"—not in his own quarrel, it is true, but in defense of a stranger unfairly beset by numbers. He had kept a sumptuous saloon. He had been the proprietor of a dashing helpmeet whom he could have discarded without the formality of a divorce. He had held a high position in the fire department and been a very Warwick in politics. When he died there was great lamentation throughout the town, but especially in the vast bottom-stratum of society.

On the inquest it was shown that Buck Fanshaw, in the delirium of a wasting typhoid fever, had taken arsenic, shot himself through the body, cut his throat, and jumped out of a four-story window and broken his neck—and after due deliberation, the jury, sad and tearful, but with intelligence unblinded by its sorrow, brought in a verdict of death "by the visitation of God." What could the world do without juries?

Prodigious preparations were made for the funeral.

All the vehicles in town were hired, all the saloons put in mourning, all the municipal and fire-company flags hung at half-mast, and all the firemen ordered to muster in uniform and bring their machines duly draped in black. Now—let us remark in parentheses—as all the peoples of the earth had representative adventurers in the Silverland, and as each adventurer had brought the slang of his nation or his locality with him, the combination made the slang of Nevada the richest and the most infinitely varied and copious that had ever existed anywhere in the world, perhaps, except in the mines of California in the "early days." Slang was the language of Nevada. It was hard to preach a sermon without it, and be understood. Such phrases as "You bet!" "Oh, no, I reckon not!" "No Irish need apply," and a hundred others, became so common as to fall from the lips of a speaker unconsciously—and very often when they did not touch the subject under discussion and consequently failed to mean anything.

After Buck Fanshaw's inquest, a meeting of the short-haired brotherhood was held, for nothing can be done on the Pacific coast without a public meeting and an expression of sentiment. Regretful resolutions were passed and various committees appointed; among others, a committee of one was deputed to call on the minister, a fragile, gentle, spiritual new fledgling from an Eastern theological seminary, and as yet unacquainted with the ways of the mines. The committeeman, "Scotty" Briggs, made his visit; and in after days it was worth something to hear the minister tell about it. Scotty was a stalwart rough, whose customary suit, when on weighty official business, like committee work, was a fire-helmet, flaming red flannel shirt, patent-leather belt with spanner and revolver attached, coat hung over arm, and pants stuffed into boot-tops. He formed something of a contrast to the pale theological student. It is fair to say of Scotty, however, in passing, that he had a warm heart, and a strong love for his friends, and never entered into a quarrel when he could reasonably keep out of it. Indeed, it was commonly

said that whenever one of Scotty's fights was inves-
tigated, it always turned out that it had originally been
no affair of his, but that out of native good-heartedness
he had dropped in of his own accord to help the man
who was getting the worst of it. He and Buck Fanshaw
were bosom friends, for years, and had often taken
adventurous "pot-luck" together. On one occasion, they
had thrown off their coats and taken the weaker side
in a fight among strangers, and after gaining a hard-
earned victory, turned and found that the men they
were helping had deserted early, and not only that,
but had stolen their coats and made off with them.
But to return to Scotty's visit to the minister. He was
on a sorrowful mission, now, and his face was the
picture of woe. Being admitted to the presence he sat
down before the clergyman, placed his fire-hat on an
unfinished manuscript sermon under the minister's
nose, took from it a red silk handkerchief, wiped his
brow and heaved a sigh of dismal impressiveness, ex-
planatory of his business. He choked, and even shed
tears; but with an effort he mastered his voice and said
in lugubrious tones:

"Are you the duck that runs the gospel-mill next
door?"

"Am I the—pardon me, I believe I do not understand?"

With another sigh and a half-sob, Scotty rejoined:

"Why you see we are in a bit of trouble, and the
boys thought maybe you would give us a lift, if we'd
tackle you—that is, if I've got the rights of it and you
are the head clerk of the doxology-works next door."

"I am the shepherd in charge of the flock whose fold
is next door."

"The which?"

"The spiritual adviser of the little company of
believers whose sanctuary adjoins these premises."

Scotty scratched his head, reflected a moment, and
then said:

"You ruther hold over me, pard. I reckon I can't call that hand. Ante and pass the buck."

"How? I beg pardon. What did I understand you to say?"

"Well, you've ruther got the bulge on me. Or maybe we've both got the bulge, somehow. You don't smoke me and I don't smoke you. You see, one of the boys has passed in his cheeks, and we want to give him a good send-off, and so the thing I'm on now is to roust out somebody to jerk a little chin-music for us and waltz him through handsome."

"My friend, I seem to grow more and more bewildered. Your observations are wholly incomprehensible to me. Cannot you simplify them in some way? At first I thought perhaps I understood you, but I grope now. Would it not expedite matters if you restricted yourself to categorical statements of fact unencumbered with obstructing accumulations of metaphor and allegory?"

Another pause, and more reflection. Then, said Scotty:

"I'll have to pass, I judge."

"How?"

"You've raised me out, pard."

"I still fail to catch your meaning."

"Why, that last lead of yourn is too many for me—that's the idea. I can't neither trump nor follow suit."

The clergyman sank back in his chair perplexed. Scotty leaned his head on his hand and gave himself up to thought. Presently his face came up, sorrowful but confident.

"I've got it now, so's you can savvy," he said. "What we want is a gospel-sharp. See?"

"A what?"

"Gospel-sharp. Parson."

"Oh! Why did you not say so before? I am a clergyman—a parson."

"Now you talk! You see my blind and straddle it like a man. Put it there!"—extending a brawny paw, which closed over the minister's small hand and gave it a shake indicative of fraternal sympathy and fervent gratification.

"Now we're all right, pard. Let's start fresh. Don't you mind my snuffling a little—becuz we're in a power of trouble. You see, one of the boys has gone up the flume—"

"Gone where?"

"Up the flume—throwed up the sponge, you understand."

"Thrown up the sponge?"

"Yes—kicked the bucket—"

"Ah—has departed to that mysterious country from whose bourne no traveler returns."

"Return! I reckon not. Why, pard, he's *dead!*"

"Yes, I understand."

"Oh, you do? Well I thought maybe you might be getting tangled some more. Yes, you see he's dead again—"

"*Again!* Why, has he ever been dead before?"

"Dead before? No! Do you reckon a man has got as many lives as a cat? But you bet you he's awful dead now, poor old boy, and I wish I'd never seen this day. I don't want no better friend than Buck Fanshaw. I knowed him by the back; and when I know a man and like him, I freeze to him—you hear *me*. Take him all round, pard, there never was a bullier man in the mines. No man ever knowed Buck Fanshaw to go back on a friend. But it's all up, you know, it's all up. It ain't no use. They've scooped him."

"Scooped him?"

"Yes—death has. Well, well, well, we've got to give him up. Yes, indeed. It's a kind of a hard world, after all, *ain't* it? But pard, he was a rustler! You ought to seen him get started once. He was a bully boy with a glass eye! Just spit in his face and give him room according to his strength, and it was just beautiful to see him peel and go in. He was the worst son of a thief that ever drawed breath. Pard, he was *on* it! He was on it bigger than an Injun!"

"On it? On what?"

"On the shoot. On the shoulder. On the fight, you understand. *He* didn't give a continental for *any*body. *Beg* your pardon, friend, for coming so near saying a cuss-word—but you see I'm on an awful strain, in this palaver, on account of having to cramp down and draw everything so mild. But we've not to give him up. There ain't any getting around that, I don't reckon. Now if we can get you to help plant him—"

"Preach the funeral discourse? Assist at the obsequies?"

"Obs'quies is good. Yes. That's it—that's our little game. We are going to get the thing up regardless, you know. He was always nifty himself, and so you bet you his funeral ain't going to be no slouch—solid-silver door-plate on his coffin, six plumes on the hearse, and a driver on the box in a biled shirt and a plug hat— how's that for high? And we'll take care of *you*, pard. We'll fix you all right. There'll be a kerridge for you; and whatever you want, you just 'scape out and we'll 'tend to it. We've got a shebang fixed up for you to stand behind, in No. 1's house, and don't you be afraid. Just go in and toot your horn, if you don't sell a clam. Put Buck through as bully as you can, pard, for anybody that knowed him will tell you that he was one of the whitest men that was ever in the mines. You can't draw it too strong. He never could stand it to see things going wrong. He's done more to make this town quiet and peaceable than any man in it. I've seen him lick four Greasers in eleven minutes, myself. If a thing wanted regulating, *he* warn't a man to go browsing around after somebody to do it, but he would prance in and regulate it himself. He warn't a Catholic. Scasely. He was down on 'em. His word was, 'No Irish need apply!' But it didn't make no difference about that when it came down to what a man's rights was—and so, when some roughs jumped the Catholic boneyard and started in to stake out town lots in it he *went* for 'em! And he *cleaned* 'em, too! I was there, pard, and I seen it myself."

"That was very well indeed—at least the impulse was —whether the act was strictly defensible or not. Had deceased any religious convictions? That is to say, did he feel a dependence upon, or acknowledge allegiance to a higher power?"

More reflection.

"I reckon you've stumped me again, pard. Could you say it over once more, and say it slow?"

"Well, to simplify it somewhat, was he, or rather had he ever been connected with any organization sequestered from secular concerns and devoted to self-sacrifice in the interests of morality?"

"All down but nine—set 'em up on the other alley, pard."

"What did I understand you to say?"

"Why, you're most too many for me, you know. When you get in with your left I hunt grass every time. Every time you draw, you fill; but I don't seem to have any luck. Let's have a new deal."

"How? Begin again?"

"That's it."

"Very well. Was he a good man, and—"

"There—I see that; don't put up another chip till I look at my hand. A good man, says you? Pard, it ain't no name for it. He was the best man that ever—pard, you would have doted on that man. He could lam any galoot of his inches in America. It was him that put down the riot last election before it got a start; and everybody said he was the only man that could have done it. He waltzed in with a spanner in one hand and a trumpet in the other, and sent fourteen men home on a shutter in less than three minutes. He had that riot all broke up and prevented nice before anybody ever got a chance to strike a blow. He was always for peace, and he would *have* peace—he could not stand disturbances. Pard, he was a great loss to this town. It would please the boys if you could chip in something like that and do him justice. Here once when the Micks got to throwing stones through the Methodis'

Sunday-school windows, Buck Fanshaw, all of his own notion, shut up his saloon and took a couple of six-shooters and mounted guard over the Sunday school. Says he, 'No Irish need apply!' And they didn't. He was the bulliest man in the mountains, pard! He could run faster, jump higher, hit harder, and hold more tanglefoot whisky without spilling it than any man in seventeen counties. Put that in, pard—it'll please the boys more than anything you could say. And you can say, pard, that he never shook his mother."

"Never shook his mother?"

"That's it—any of the boys will tell you so."

"Well, but why *should* he shake her?"

"That's what *I* say—but some people does."

"Not people of any repute?"

"Well, some that averages pretty so-so."

"In my opinion the man that would offer personal violence to his own mother, ought to—"

"Cheese it, pard; you've banked your ball clean outside the string. What I was a drivin' at, was, that he never *throwed off* on his mother—don't you see? No indeedy. He give her a house to live in, and town lots, and plenty of money; and he looked after her and took care of her all the time; and when she was down with the smallpox I'm d——d if he didn't set up nights and nuss her himself! *Beg* your pardon for saying it, but it hopped out too quick for yours truly. You've treated me like a gentleman, pard, and I ain't the man to hurt your feelings intentional. I think you're white. I think you're a square man, pard. I like you, and I'll lick any man that don't. I'll lick him till he can't tell himself from a last year's corpse! Put it *there!*" [Another fraternal handshake—and exit.]

The obsequies were all that "the boys" could desire. Such a marvel of funeral pomp had never been seen in Virginia. The plumed hearse, the dirge-breathing brass bands, the closed marts of business, the flags drooping at half-mast, the long, plodding procession of uniformed secret societies, military battalions and fire companies, draped engines, carriages of officials, and citizens in vehicles and on foot, attracted multitudes of spectators to the sidewalks, roofs, and windows; and for years afterward, the degree of grandeur attained by any civic display in Virginia was determined by comparison with Buck Fanshaw's funeral.

Scotty Briggs, as a pall-bearer and a mourner, occupied a prominent place at the funeral, and when the sermon was finished and the last sentence of the prayer for the dead man's soul ascended, he responded, in a low voice, but with feeling:

"*Amen.* No Irish need apply."

As the bulk of the response was without apparent relevancy, it was probably nothing more than a humble tribute to the memory of the friend that was gone; for, as Scotty head once said, it was "his word."

Scotty Briggs, in after days, achieved the distinction of becoming the only convert to religion that was ever gathered from the Virginia roughs; and it transpired that the man who had it in him to espouse the quarrel of the weak out of inborn nobility of spirit was no mean timber whereof to construct a Christian. The making him one did not warp his generosity or diminish his courage; on the contrary it gave intelligent direction to the one and a broader field to the other. If his Sunday-school class progressed faster than the other classes, was it matter for wonder? I think not. He talked to his pioneer small-fry in a language they understood! It was my large privilege, a month before he died, to hear him tell the beautiful story of Joseph and his brethren to his class "without looking at the book." I leave it to the reader to fancy what it was like, as it fell, riddled with slang, from the lips of that grave, earnest teacher, and was listened to by his little learners with a consuming interest that showed that they were as unconscious as he was that any violence was being done to the sacred proprieties!

From *Roughing It,* 1872

MRS. McWILLIAMS AND
THE LIGHTNING

Well, sir—continued Mr. McWilliams, for this was not
the beginning of his talk—the fear of lightning is one
of the most distressing infirmities a human being can
be afflicted with. It is mostly confined to women; but
now and then you find it in a little dog, and sometimes
in a man. It is a particularly distressing infirmity, for
the reason that it takes the sand out of a person to an
extent which no other fear can, and it can't be *reasoned*
with, and neither can it be shamed out of a person. A
woman who could face the very devil himself—or a
mouse—loses her grip and goes all to pieces in front
of a flash of lightning. Her fright is something pitiful
to see.

Well, as I was telling you, I woke up, with that
smothered and unlocatable cry of "Mortimer! Mortimer!" wailing in my ears; and as soon as I could scrape
my faculties together I reached over in the dark and
then said:

"Evangeline, is that you calling? What is the matter?
Where are you?"

"Shut up in the boot-closet. You ought to be
ashamed to lie there and sleep so, and such an awful
storm going on."

"Why, how *can* one be ashamed when he is asleep?
It is unreasonable; a man *can't* be ashamed when he is
asleep, Evangeline."

"You never try, Mortimer—you know very well you
never try."

I caught the sound of muffled sobs.

47

That sound smote dead the sharp speech that was on my lips, and I changed it to—

"I'm sorry, dear—I'm truly sorry. I never meant to act so. Come back and—"

"*Mortimer!*"

"Heavens! what is the matter, my love?"

"Do you mean to say you are in that bed yet?"

"Why, of course."

"Come out of it instantly. I should think you would take some *little* care fo your life, for *my* sake and the children's, if you will not for your own."

"But, my love—"

"Don't talk to me, Mortimer. You *know* there is no place so dangerous as a bed in such a thunderstorm as this—all the books say that; yet there you would lie, and deliberately throw away your life—for goodness knows what, unless for the sake of arguing, and arguing, and—"

"But, confound it, Evangeline, I'm *not* in the bed now. I'm—"

[Sentence interrupted by a sudden glare of lightning, followed by a terrified little scream from Mrs. Mc-Williams and a tremendous blast of thunder.]

"There! You see the result. Oh, Mortimer, how *can* you be so profligate as to swear at such a time as this?"

"I *didn't* swear. And that *wasn't* a result of it, anyway. It would have come, just the same, if I hadn't said a word; and you know very well, Evangeline—at least, you ought to know—that when the atmosphere is charged with electricity—"

"Oh, yes; now argue it, and argue it, and argue it! —I don't see how you can act so, when you *know* there is not a lightning-rod on the place, and your poor wife and children are absolutely at the mercy of Providence. What *are* you doing?—lighting a match at such a time as this! Are you stark mad?"

"Hang it, woman, where's the harm? The place is as dark as the inside of an infidel, and—"

"Put it out! put it out instantly! Are you determined to sacrifice us all? You *know* there is nothing attracts lightning like a light. [*Fzt!—crash! boom—boloom-boom-boom!*] Oh, just hear it! Now you see what you've done!"

"No, I *don't* see what I've done. A match may attract lightning, for all I know, but it don't *cause* lightning— I'll go odds on that. And it didn't attract it worth a cent this time; for if that shot was leveled at my match, it was blessed poor marksmanship—about an average of none out of a possible million, I should say. Why, at Dollymount such marksmanship as that—"

"For shame, Mortimer! Here we are standing right in the very presence of death, and yet in so solemn a moment you are capable of using such language as that. If you have no desire to— Mortimer!"

"Well?"

"Did you say your prayers tonight?"

"I—I—meant to, but I got to trying to cipher out how much twelve times thirteen is, and—"

[*Fzt!—boom - berroom - boom! bumble - umble bang-*SMASH!]

"Oh, we are lost, beyond all help! How *could* you neglect such a thing at such a time as this?"

"But it *wasn't* 'such a time as this.' There wasn't a cloud in the sky. How could *I* know there was going to be all this rumpus and pow-wow about a little slip like that? And I don't think it's just fair for you to make so much out of it, anyway, seeing it happens so seldom; I haven't missed before since I brought on that earthquake, four years ago."

"*Mortimer!* How you talk! Have you forgotten the yellow-fever?"

"My dear, you are always throwing up the yellow-fever to me, and I think it is perfectly unreasonable. You can't even send a telegraphic message as far as Memphis without relays, so how is a little devotional slip of mine going to carry so far? I'll *stand* the earthquake, because it was in the neighborhood; but I'll be hanged if I'm going to be responsible for every blamed—"

[*Fzt!*—BOOM *beroom*-boom! boom.—BANG!]

"Oh, dear, dear, dear! I *know* it struck something, Mortimer. We never shall see the light of another day; and if it will do you any good to remember, when we are gone, that your dreadful language—*Mortimer!*"

"*Well!* What now?"

"Your voice sounds as if— Mortimer, are you actually standing in front of that open fireplace?"

"That is the very crime I am committing."

"Get away from it this moment! You do seem determined to bring destruction on us all. Don't you *know* that there is no better conductor for lightning than an open chimney? *Now* where have you got to?"

"I'm here by the window."

"Oh, for pity's sake! have you lost your mind? Clear out from there, this moment! The very children in arms know it is fatal to stand near a window in a thunderstorm. Dear, dear, I know I shall never see the light of another day! Mortimer!"

"Yes."

"What is that rustling?"

"It's me."

"What are you doing?"

"Trying to find the upper end of my pantaloons."

"Quick! throw those things away! I do believe you would deliberately put on those clothes at such a time as this; yet you know perfectly well that *all* authorities agree that woolen stuffs attract lightning. Oh, dear, dear, it isn't sufficient that one's life must be in peril from natural causes, but you must do everything you can possibly think of to augment the danger. Oh, *don't* sing! What *can* you be thinking of?"

"Now where's the harm in it?"

"Mortimer, if I have told you once, I have told you a hundred times, that singing causes vibrations in the atmosphere which interrupt the flow of the electric fluid, and— What on *earth* are you opening that door for?"

"Goodness gracious, woman, is there any harm in *that?*"

"*Harm?* There's *death* in it. Anybody that has given this subject any attention knows that to create a draught is to invite the lightning. You haven't half shut it; shut it *tight*—and do hurry, or we are all destroyed. Oh, it is an awful thing to be shut up with a lunatic at such a time as this. Mortimer, what *are* you doing?"

"Nothing. Just turning on the water. This room is smothering hot and close. I want to bathe my face and hands."

"You have certainly parted with the remnant of your mind! Where lightning strikes any other substance once, it strikes water fifty times. Do turn it off. Oh, dear, I am sure that nothing in this world can save us. It does seem to me that—Mortimer, what was that?"

"It was a da—it was a picture. Knocked it down."

"Then you are close to the wall! I never heard of such imprudence! Don't you *know* that there's no better conductor for lightning than a wall? Come away from there! And you came as near as anything to swearing, too. Oh, how can you be so desperately wicked, and your family in such peril? Mortimer, did you order a feather bed, as I asked you to do?"

"No. Forgot it."

"Forgot it! It may cost you your life. If you had a feather bed now, and could spread it in the middle of the room and lie on it, you would be perfectly safe. Come in here—come quick, before you have a chance to commit any more frantic indiscretions."

I tried, but the little closet would not hold us both with the door shut, unless we could be content to smother. I gasped awhile, then forced my way out. My wife called out:

"Mortimer, something *must* be done for your preservation. Give me that German book that is on the end of the mantelpiece, and a candle; but don't light it; give me a match; I will light it in here. That book has some directions in it."

I got the book—at cost of a vase and some other

brittle things; and the madam shut herself up with her candle. I had a moment's peace; then she called out:

"Mortimer, what was that?"

"Nothing but the cat."

"The cat! Oh, destruction! Catch her, and shut her up in the washstand. Do be quick, love; cats are *full* of electricity. I just know my hair will turn white with this night's awful perils."

I heard the muffled sobbings again. But for that, I should not have moved hand or foot in such a wild enterprise in the dark.

However, I went at my task—over chairs, and against all sorts of obstructions, all of them hard ones, too, and most of them with sharp edges—and at last I got kitty cooped up in the commode, at an expense of over four hundred dollars in broken furniture and shins. Then these muffled words came from the closet:

"It says the safest thing is to stand on a chair in the middle of the room, Mortimer; and the legs of the chair must be insulated with non-conductors. That is, you must set the legs of the chair in glass tumblers. [*Fzt!—boom—bang!—smash!*] Oh, hear that! Do hurry, Mortimer, before you are struck."

I managed to find and secure the tumblers. I got the last four—broke all the rest. I insulated the chair legs, and called for further instructions.

"Mortimer, it says, '*Während eines Gewitters entferne man Metalle, wie z. B., Ringe, Uhren, Schlüssel, etc., von sich und halte sich auch nicht an solchen Stellen auf, wo viele Metalle bei einander liegen, oder mit andern Körpern verbunden sind, wie an Herden, Oefen, Eisengittern u. dgl.*' What does that mean, Mortimer? Does it mean that you must keep metals *about* you, or keep them *away* from you?"

"Well, I hardly know. It appears to be a little mixed. All German advice is more or less mixed. However, I think that that sentence is mostly in the dative case, with a little genitive and accusative sifted in, here and there, for luck; so I reckon it means that you must keep some metals *about* you."

"Yes, that must be it. It stands to reason that it is. They are in the nature of lightning-rods, you know. Put on your fireman's helmet, Mortimer; that is mostly metal."

I got it, and put it on—a very heavy and clumsy and uncomfortable thing on a hot night in a close room. Even my night-dress seemed to be more clothing than I strictly needed.

"Mortimer, I think your middle ought to be protected. Won't you buckle on your militia saber, please?"

I complied.

"Now, Mortimer, you ought to have some way to protect your feet. Do please put on your spurs."

I did it—in silence—and kept my temper as well as I could.

"Mortimer, it says, '*Das Gewitter läuten ist sehr gefährlich, weil die Glocke selbst, sowie der durch das Läuten veranlasste Luftzug und die Höhe des Thurmes den Blitz anziehen könnten.*' Mortimer, does that mean that it is dangerous not to ring the church bells during a thunderstorm?"

"Yes, it seems to mean that—if that is the past participle of the nominative case singular, and I reckon it is. Yes, I think it means that on account of the height of the church tower and the absence of *Luftzug* it would be very dangerous (*sehr gefährlich*) not to ring the bells in time of a storm; and, moreover, don't you see, the very wording—"

"Never mind that, Mortimer; don't waste the precious time in talk. Get the large dinner-bell; it is right there in the hall. Quick, Mortimer, dear; we are almost safe. Oh, dear, I do believe we are going to be saved, at last!"

Our little summer establishment stands on top of a high range of hills, overlooking a valley. Several farmhouses are in our neighborhood—the nearest some three or four hundred yards away.

When I, mounted on the chair, had been clanging that dreadful bell a matter of seven or eight minutes, our shutters were suddenly torn open from without, and a brilliant bull's-eye lantern was thrust in at the window, followed by a hoarse inquiry:

"What in the nation is the matter here?"

The window was full of men's heads, and the heads were full of eyes that stared wildly at my night-dress and my warlike accoutrements.

I dropped the bell, skipped down from the chair in confusion, and said:

"There is nothing the matter, friends—only a little discomfort on account of the thunderstorm. I was trying to keep off the lightning."

"Thunderstorm? Lightning? Why, Mr. McWilliams, have you lost your mind? It is a beautiful starlight night; there has been no storm."

I looked out, and I was so astonished I could hardly speak for a while. Then I said:

"I do not understand this. We distinctly saw the glow of the flashes through the curtains and shutters, and heard the thunder."

One after another of those people lay down on the ground to laugh—and two of them died. One of the survivors remarked:

"Pity you didn't think to open your blinds and look over to the top of the high hill yonder. What you heard was cannon; what you saw was the flash. You see, the telegraph brought some news, just at midnight; Garfield's nominated—and that's what's the matter!"

Yes, Mr. Twain, as I was saying in the beginning (said Mr. McWilliams), the rules for preserving people against lightning are so excellent and so innumerable that the most incomprehensible thing in the world to me is how anybody ever manages to get struck.

So saying, he gathered up his satchel and umbrella, and departed; for the train had reached his town.

Anonymous

Outstanding among the mythical heroes of American folklore is Paul Bunyan, the "mightiest of loggers." The origins of this demigod are clouded and remote. There is some indication that a French Canadian logger of the 1830s might have been the original Paul Bunyan—if, indeed, there ever was a real-life Bunyan. Various accounts of his antics and achievements were shared far and wide. By the time Paul Bunyan stories were first published in the *Detroit News-Tribune* in 1910, he was known to lumbermen from Pennsylvania to Wisconsin and on into the Northwest. In 1914, the Red River Lumber Company distributed a booklet of Bunyan stories compiled and illustrated by W. B. Laughead, which they used to publicize their products. Since then, many other writers have issued their versions of the legend in both story and verse.

PAUL BUNYAN—
THE WHISTLING RIVER

It seems that some years before the winter of the Blue Snow (which every old logger remembers because of a heavy fall of bright blue snow which melted to ink, giving folks the idea of writing stories like these, so they tell) Ol' Paul was logging on what was then known as the Whistling River. It got its name from the fact that every morning, right on the dot, at nineteen minutes after five, and every night at ten minutes past six, it r'ared up to a height of two hundred and seventy-three feet and let loose a whistle that could be heard for a distance of six hundred and three miles in any direction.

Of course, if one man listening by himself can hear that far, it seems reasonable to suppose that two men listening together can hear it just twice as far. They tell me that even as far away as Alaska, most every camp had from two to four whistle-listeners (as many as were needed to hear the whistle without straining), who got two bits a listen and did nothing but listen for the right time, especially quitting time.

However, it seems that the river was famous for more than its whistling, for it was known as the orneriest river that ever ran between two banks. It seemed to take a fiendish delight in tying whole rafts of good saw logs into more plain and fancy knots than forty-three old sailors even knew the names of. It was an old "side winder" for fair. Even so, it is unlikely that Ol' Paul would ever have bothered with it, if it had left his beard alone.

It happened this way. It seems that Ol' Paul is sitting on a low hill one afternoon, combing his great curly beard with a pine tree, while he plans his winter operations. All of a sudden like, and without a word of warning, the river h'ists itself up on its hind legs and squirts about four thousand five hundred and nineteen gallons of river water straight in the center of Ol' Paul's whiskers.

Naturally Paul's considerably startled, but says nothing, figuring that if he pays it no mind, it'll go 'way and leave him be. But no sooner does he get settled back with his thinking and combing again, than the durn river squirts some more! This time, along with the water, it throws in for good measure a batch of mud turtles, thirteen large carp, a couple of drowned muskrat, and half a raft of last year's saw logs. By this time Ol' Paul is pretty mad, and he jumps up and lets loose a yell that causes a landslide out near Pike's Peak, and startles a barber in Missouri so he cuts half the hair off the minister's toupee, causing somewhat of a stir thereabouts. Paul stomps around waving his arms for a spell, and allows:

"By the Gee-Jumpin' John Henry and the Great Horn Spoon, I'll tame that river or bust a gallus tryin'."

He goes over to another hill and sits down to think out a way to tame a river, forgetting his winter operations entirely. He sits there for three days and forty-seven hours without moving, thinking at top speed all the while, and finally comes to the conclusion that the best thing to do is to take out the kinks. But he knows that taking the kinks out of a river as tricky as this one is apt to be quite a chore, so he keeps on sitting there while he figures out ways and means. Of course, he could dig a new channel and run the river through that, but that was never Paul's way. He liked to figure out new ways of doing things, even if they were harder.

Meanwhile he's gotten a mite hungry, so he hollers down to camp for Sourdough Sam to bring him up a little popcorn, of which he is very fond. So Sam

hitches up a four-horse team while his helpers are
popping the corn, and soon arrives at Paul's feet with
a wagon load.

Paul eats popcorn and thinks. The faster he thinks
the faster he eats, and the faster he eats the faster he
thinks, until finally his hands are moving so fast that
nothing shows but a blur, and they make a wind that
is uprooting trees all around him. His chewing sounds
like a couple hundred coffee grinders all going at once.
In practically no time at all the ground for three miles
and a quarter in every direction is covered to a depth
of eighteen inches with popcorn scraps, and several
thousand small birds and animals, seeing the ground
all white and the air filled with what looks like
snowflakes, conclude that a blizzard is upon them and
immediately freeze to death, furnishing the men with
pot pies for some days.

But to get back to Ol' Paul's problem. Just before
the popcorn is all gone, he decides that the only
practical solution is to hitch Babe, the Mighty Blue Ox,
to the river and let him yank it straight.

Babe was so strong that he could pull mighty near
anything that could be hitched to. His exact size, as
I said before, is not known, for although it is said that
he stood ninety-three hands high, it's not known
whether that meant ordinary logger's hands, or hands
the size of Paul's, which, of course, would be something else again.

However, they tell of an eagle that had been in the
habit of roosting on the tip of Babe's right horn,
suddenly deciding to fly to the other. Columbus Day,
it was, when he started. He flew steadily, so they say,
night and day, fair weather and foul, until his wing
feathers were worn down to pinfeathers and a new set
grew to replace them. In all, he seems to have worn
out seventeen sets of feathers on the trip, and from
reaching up to brush the sweat out of his eyes so
much, had worn all the feathers off the top of his head,
becoming completely bald, as are all of his descendants

to this day. Finally the courageous bird won through, reaching the brass ball on the tip of the left horn on the seventeenth of March. He waved a wing weakly at the cheering lumberjacks and 'lowed as how he'd of made it sooner but for the head winds.

But the problem is how to hitch Babe to the river, as it's a well-known fact that an ordinary log chain and skid hook will not hold water. So after a light lunch of three sides of barbecued beef, half a wagon load of potatoes, carrots and a few other odds and ends, Ol' Paul goes down to the blacksmith shop and gets Ole, the Big Swede, to help him look through the big instruction book that came with the woods and tells how to do most everything under the sun. But though Paul reads the book through from front to back twice while Ole reads it from back to front, and they both read it once from bottom to top, they find nary a word about how to hook onto a river. However, they do find an old almanac stuck between the pages and get so busy reading up on the weather for the coming year, and a lot of fancy ailments of one kind and another that it's supper time before they know it, and the problem's still unsolved. So Paul decides that the only practical thing to do is to invent a rigging of some kind himself.

At any rate he has to do something, as every time he hears the river whistle, it makes him so mad he's fit to be tied, which interferes with his work more than something. No one can do their best under such conditions.

Being as how this was sort of a special problem, he thought it out in a special way. Paul was like that. As he always thought best when he walked, he had the men survey a circle about thirty miles in diameter to walk around. This was so that if he was quite a while thinking it out he wouldn't be finding himself way down in Australia when he'd finished.

When everything is ready, he sets his old fur cap tight on his head, clasps his hands behind him, and starts walking and thinking. He thinks and walks. The faster he walks the faster he thinks. He makes a complete circle every half hour. By morning he's worn a path that is knee-deep even on him, and he has to call the men to herd the stock away and keep them from falling in and getting crippled. Three days later he thinks it out, but he's worn himself down so deep that it takes a day and a half to get a ladder built that will reach down that far. When he does get out, he doesn't even wait for breakfast, but whistles for Babe and tears right out across the hills to the north.

The men have no idea what he intends to do, but they know from experience that it'll be good, so they cheer till their throats are so sore they have to stay around the mess hall drinking Paul's private barrel of cough syrup till supper time. And after that they go to bed and sleep very soundly.

Paul and the Ox travel plenty fast, covering twenty-four townships at a stride, and the wind from their passing raises a dust that doesn't even begin to settle for some months. There are those who claim that the present dust storms are nothing more or less than that same dust just beginning to get back to earth—but that's a matter of opinion. About noon, as they near the North Pole, they begin to see blizzard tracks, and in a short time are in the very heart of their summer feeding grounds. Taking a sack from his shoulder, Paul digs out materials for a box trap, which he sets near a well-traveled blizzard trail, and baits with fresh icicles from the top of the North Pole. Then he goes away to eat his lunch, but not until he's carefully brushed out his tracks—a trick he later taught the Indians.

After lunch he amuses himself for a while by throwing huge chunks of ice into the water for Babe to retrieve, but he soon has to whistle the great beast out, as every time he jumps into the water he causes such a splash that a tidal wave threatens Galveston, Texas, which at that time was inhabited by nobody in particular. Some of the ice he threw in is still floating around the ocean, causing plenty of excitement for the iceberg patrol.

About two o'clock he goes back to his blizzard trap and discovers that he has caught seven half-grown blizzards and one grizzled old nor'wester, which is raising considerable fuss and bids fair to trample the young ones before he can get them out. But he finally manages to get a pair of half-grown ones in his sack and turns the others loose.

About midnight he gets back to camp, and hollers at Ole, the Big Swede:

"Build me the biggest log chain that's ever been built, while I stake out these dad-blasted blizzards! We're goin' to warp it to 'er proper, come mornin'."

Then he goes down to the foot of the river and pickets one of the blizzards to a tree on the bank, then crosses and ties the other directly opposite. Right away the river begins to freeze. In ten minutes the slush ice reaches nearly from bank to bank, and the blizzards are not yet really warmed to their work, either. Paul watches for a few minutes, and then goes back to camp to warm up, feeling mighty well satisfied with the way things are working out.

In the morning the river has a tough time r'aring up for what it maybe knows to be its last whistle, for its foot is frozen solid for more than seventeen miles. The blizzards have really done the business.

By the time breakfast is over, the great chain's ready and Babe all harnessed. Paul quick like wraps one end of the chain seventy-two times around the foot of the river, and hitches Babe to the other. Warning the men to stand clear, he shouts at the Ox to pull. But though the great beast strains till his tongue hangs out, pulling the chain out into a solid bar some seven and a half miles long, and sinks knee-deep in the solid rock, the river stubbornly refuses to budge, hanging onto its kinks like a snake in a gopher hole. Seeing this, Ol' Paul grabs the chain and, letting

loose a holler that blows the tarpaper off the shacks
in the Nebraska sandhills, he and the Ox together
give a mighty yank that jerks the river loose from end
to end, and start hauling it out across the prairie so
fast that it smokes.

After a time Paul comes back and sights along the
river, which now is as straight as a gun barrel. But he
doesn't have long to admire his work, for he soon finds
he has another problem on his hands. You see, it's this
way. A straight river is naturally much shorter than
a crooked one, and now all the miles and miles of
extra river that used to be in the kinks are running wild
out on the prairie. This galls the farmers in those parts
more than a little. So it looks like Paul had better
figure something out, and mighty soon at that, for
already he can see clouds of dust the prairie folks are
raising as they come at top speed to claim damages.

After three minutes of extra deep thought he sends
a crew to camp to bring his big cross-cut saw and a lot
of baling wire. He saws the river into nine-mile lengths
and the men roll it up like linoleum and tie it with the
wire. Some say he used these later when he logged off
the desert, rolling out as many lengths as he needed to
float his logs. But that's another story.

But his troubles with the Whistling River were not
all over. It seems that being straightened sort of took
the gimp out of the river, and from that day on it
refused to whistle even a bird call. And as Paul had
gotten into the habit of depending on the whistle to
wake up the men in the morning, things were a mite
upset.

First he hired an official getter-upper who rode
through the camp on a horse, and beat a triangle. But
the camp was so big that it took three hours and
seventy-odd minutes to make the trip. Naturally some
of the men were called too early and some too late.
It's hard to say what might have happened if Squeaky
Swanson hadn't showed up about that time. His speaking voice was a thin squeak, but when he hollered he

could be heard clear out to Kansas on a still day. So every morning he stood outside the cook-shack and hollered the blankets off every bunk in camp. Naturally the men didn't stay in bed long after the blankets were off them, what with the cold wind and all, so Squeaky was a great success and for years did nothing but holler in the mornings.

O. Henry
[1862–1910]

The ironic, unexpected ending is the hallmark of O. Henry's short stories. He is also noted for his careful plotting, his clever use of coincidence, and his warm sympathy for the underdog. Born William Sidney Porter in Greensboro, North Carolina, he worked in Texas as a clerk, draftsman, reporter and columnist until 1896, when he was indicted for the embezzlement of funds at a bank where he had been a teller. He escaped to New Orleans and later to Honduras, where he joined two famous outlaws, the Jennings brothers, on their travels through South America and Mexico. He returned to the United States when he learned of his wife's fatal illness and was sentenced to three years in prison. It is while there that he first made his reputation as a short story writer under the pen name O. Henry. After leaving prison in 1901, he settled in New York City, where he completed 600 stories before his death from tuberculosis.

THE RANSOM OF RED CHIEF

It looked like a good thing: but wait till I tell you. We were down South, in Alabama—Bill Driscoll and myself —when this kidnapping idea struck us. It was, as Bill afterward expressed it, "during a moment of temporary mental apparition"; but we didn't find that out till later.

There was a town down there, as flat as a flannel-cake, and called Summit, of course. It contained inhabitants of as undeleterious and self-satisfied a class of peasantry as ever clustered around a Maypole.

Bill and me had a joint capital of about six hundred dollars, and we needed just two thousand dollars more to pull off a fraudulent town-lot scheme in Western Illinois. We talked it over on the front steps of the hotel. Philoprogenitoveness, says we, is strong in semi-rural communities; therefore, and for other reasons, a kidnapping project ought to do better there than in the radius of newspapers that send reporters out in plain clothes to stir up talk about such things. We knew that Summit couldn't get after us with anything stronger than constables and, maybe, some lackadaisical blood-hounds and a diatribe or two in the *Weekly Farmers' Budget.* So, it looked good.

We selected for our victim the only child of a prominent citizen named Ebenezer Dorset. The father was respectable and tight, a mortgage financier and a stern, upright collection-plate passer and forecloser. The kid was a boy of ten, with bas-relief freckles, and hair the color of the cover of the magazine you buy at the news-stand when you want to catch a train. Bill and me figured that Ebenezer would melt down for a ransom of two thousand dollars to a cent. But wait till I tell you.

About two miles from Summit was a little mountain, covered with a dense cedar brake. On the rear elevation of this mountain was a cave. There we stored provisions.

One evening after sundown, we drove in a buggy past old Dorset's house. The kid was in the street, throwing rocks at a kitten on the opposite fence.

"Hey, little boy!" says Bill, "would you like to have a bag of candy and a nice ride?"

The boy catches Bill neatly in the eye with a piece of brick.

"That will cost the old man an extra five hundred dollars," says Bill, climbing over the wheel.

That boy put up a fight like a welter-weight cinnamon bear; but, at last, we got him down in the bottom of the buggy and drove away. We took him up to the cave, and I hitched the horse in the cedar brake. After dark I drove the buggy to the little village, three miles away, where we had hired it, and walked back to the mountain.

Bill was pasting court-plaster over the scratches and bruises on his features. There was a fire burning behind the big rock at the entrance of the cave, and the boy was watching a pot of boiling coffee, with two buzzard tail-feathers stuck in his red hair. He points a stick at me when I come up, and says:

"Ha! cursed paleface, do you dare to enter the camp of Red Chief, the terror of the plains?"

"He's all right now," says Bill, rolling up his trousers and examining some bruises on his shins. "We're playing Indian. We're making Buffalo Bill's show look like magic-lantern views of Palestine in the town hall. I'm Old Hank, the Trapper, Red Chief's captive, and I'm to be scalped at daybreak. By Geronimo! That kid can kick hard."

Yes, sir, that boy seemed to be having the time of his life. The fun of camping out in a cave had made him forget that he was a captive himself. He immediately christened me Snake-eye, the Spy, and announced that, when his braves returned from the warpath, I was to be broiled at the stake at the rising of the sun.

Then we had supper; and he filled his mouth full of bacon and bread and gravy, and began to talk. He made a during-dinner speech something like this:

"I like this fine. I never camped out before; but I had a pet 'possum once, and I was nine last birthday. I hate to go to school. Rats ate up sixteen of Jimmy Talbot's aunt's speckled hen's eggs. Are there any real Indians in these woods? I want some more gravy. Does the trees moving make the wind blow? We had five puppies. What makes your nose so red, Hank? My father has lots of money. Are the stars hot? I whipped Ed Walker twice, Saturday. I don't like girls. You dassent catch toads unless with a string. Do oxen make any noise? Why are oranges round? Have you got beds to sleep on in this cave? Amos Murray has got six toes. A parrot can talk, but a monkey or a fish can't. How many does it take to make twelve?"

Every few minutes he would remember that he was a pesky redskin, and pick up his stick rifle and tiptoe to the mouth of the cave to rubber for the scouts of the hated paleface. Now and then he would let out a war-whoop that made Old Hank the Trapper shiver. That boy had Bill terrorized from the start.

"Red Chief," says I to the kid, "would you like to go home?"

"Aw, what for?" says he. "I don't have any fun at home. I hate to go to school. I like to camp out. You won't take me back home again, Snake-eye, will you?"

"Not right away," says I. "We'll stay here in the cave awhile."

"All right!" says he. "That'll be fine. I never had such fun in all my life."

We went to bed about eleven o'clock. We spread down some wide blankets and quilts and put Red Chief between us. We weren't afraid he'd run away. He kept us awake for three hours, jumping up and reaching for his rifle and screeching: "Hist! pard," in mine and Bill's ears, as the fancied crackle of a twig or the rustle of a leaf revealed to his young imagination the stealthy approach of the outlaw band. At last, I fell into a troubled sleep, and dreamed that I had been kidnapped and chained to a tree by a ferocious pirate with red hair.

Just at daybreak, I was awakened by a series of awful screams from Bill. They weren't yells, or howls, or shouts, or whoops, or yawps, such as you'd expect from a manly set of vocal organs—they were simply indecent, terrifying, humiliating screams, such as women emit when they see ghosts or caterpillars. It's an awful thing to hear a strong, desperate, fat man scream incontinently in a cave at daybreak.

I jumped up to see what the matter was. Red Chief was sitting on Bill's chest, with one hand twined in Bill's hair. In the other he had the sharp case-knife we used for slicing bacon; and he was industriously and realistically trying to take Bill's scalp, according to the sentence that had been pronounced upon him the evening before.

I got the knife away from the kid and made him lie down again. But, from that moment, Bill's spirit was broken. He laid down on his side of the bed, but he never closed an eye again in sleep as long as that boy was with us. I dozed off for awhile, but along toward sunup I remembered that Red Chief had said I was to be burned at the stake at the rising of the sun. I wasn't nervous or afraid; but I sat up and lit my pipe and leaned against a rock.

"What you getting up so soon for, Sam?" asked Bill.

"Me?" says I. "Oh, I got a kind of pain in my shoulder. I thought sitting up would rest it."

"You're a liar!" says Bill. "You're afraid. You was to be burned at sunrise, and you was afraid he'd do it. And he would, too, if he could find a match. Ain't it awful, Sam? Do you think anybody will pay out money to get a little imp like that back home?"

"Sure," said I. "A rowdy kid like that is just the kind that parents dote on. Now, you and the Chief get up and cook breakfast, while I go up on the top of this mountain and reconnoitre."

I went up on the peak of the little mountain and ran my eye over the contiguous vicinity. Over toward Summit I expected to see the sturdy yeomanry of the village armed with scythes and pitchforks beating the countryside for the dastardly kidnappers. But what I saw was a peaceful landscape dotted with one man ploughing with a dun mule. Nobody was dragging the creek; no couriers dashed hither and yon, bringing tidings of no news to the distracted parents. There was a sylvan attitude of somnolent sleepiness pervading that section of the external outward surface of Alabama that lay exposed to my view. "Perhaps," says I to myself, "it has not yet been discovered that the wolves have borne away the tender lambkin from the fold. Heaven help the wolves!" says I, and I went down the mountain to breakfast.

When I got to the cave I found Bill backed up against the side of it, breathing hard, and the boy threatening to smash him with a rock half as big as a cocoanut.

"He put a red-hot boiled potato down my back," explained Bill, "and then mashed it with his foot; and I boxed his ears. Have you got a gun about you, Sam?"

I took the rock away from the boy and kind of patched up the argument. "I'll fix you," says the kid to Bill. "No man ever yet struck the Red Chief but he got paid for it. You better beware!"

After breakfast the kid takes a piece of leather with strings wrapped around it out of his pocket and goes outside the cave unwinding it.

"What's he up to now?" says Bill, anxiously. "You don't think he'll run away, do you, Sam?"

"No fear of it," says I. "He don't seem to be much of a homebody. But we've got to fix up some plan about the ransom. There don't seem to be much excitement around Summit on account of his disappearance; but maybe they haven't realized yet that he's gone. His folks may think he's spending the night with Aunt Jane or one of the neighbors. Anyhow, he'll be missed today. Tonight we must get a message to his father demanding the two thousand dollars for his return."

Just then we heard a kind of war-whoop, such as David might have emitted when he knocked out the champion Goliath. It was a sling that Red Chief had pulled out of his pocket, and he was whirling it around his head.

I dodged, and heard a heavy thud and a kind of a sigh from Bill, like a horse gives out when you take his saddle off. A niggerhead rock the size of an egg had caught Bill just behind his left ear. He loosened himself all over and fell in the fire across the frying pan of hot water for washing the dishes. I dragged him out and poured cold water on his head for half an hour.

By and by, Bill sits up and feels behind his ear and says: "Sam, do you know who my favorite Biblical character is?"

"Take it easy," says I. "You'll come to your senses presently."

"King Herod," says he. "You won't go away and leave me here alone, will you, Sam?"

I went out and caught that boy and shook him until his freckles rattled.

"If you don't behave," says I, "I'll take you straight home. Now, are you going to be good, or not?"

"I was only funning," says he, sullenly. "I didn't mean to hurt Old Hank. But what did he hit me for? I'll behave, Snake-eye, if you won't send me home, and if you'll let me play the Black Scout today."

"I don't know the game," says I. "That's for you and Mr. Bill to decide. He's your playmate for the day. I'm going away for a while, on business. Now, you come in and make friends with him and say you are sorry for hurting him, or home you go, at once."

I made him and Bill shake hands, and then I took Bill aside and told him I was going to Poplar Grove, a little village three miles from the cave, and find out what I could about how the kidnapping had been regarded in Summit. Also, I thought it best to send a peremptory letter to old man Dorset that day, demanding the ransom and dictating how it should be paid.

"You know, Sam," says Bill, "I've stood by you without batting an eye in earthquakes, fire and flood—in poker games, dynamite outrages, police raids, train robberies, and cyclones. I never lost my nerve yet till we kidnapped that two-legged skyrocket of a kid. He's got me going. You won't leave me long with him, will you, Sam?"

"I'll be back some time this afternoon," says I. "You must keep the boy amused and quiet till I return. And now we'll write the letter to old Dorset."

Bill and I got paper and pencil and worked on the letter while Red Chief, with a blanket wrapped around him, strutted up and down, guarding the mouth of the cave. Bill begged me tearfully to make the ransom fifteen hundred dollars instead of two thousand. "I ain't attempting," says he, "to decry the celebrated moral aspect of parental affection, but we're dealing with humans, and it ain't human for anybody to give up two thousand dollars for that forty-pound chunk of freckled wildcat. I'm willing to take a chance at fifteen hundred dollars. You can charge the difference up to me."

So, to relieve Bill, I acceded, and we collaborated a letter that ran this way:

Ebenezer Dorset, Esq.:

We have your boy concealed in a place far from Summit. It is useless for you or the most skillful detectives to attempt to find him. Absolutely, the only terms on which you can have him restored to you are these: We demand fifteen hundred dollars in large bills for his return; the money to be left at midnight tonight at the same spot and in the same box as your reply—as hereinafter described. If you agree to these terms, send your answer in writing by a solitary messenger tonight at half-past eight o'clock. After crossing Owl Creek on the road to Poplar Grove, there are three large trees about a hundred yards apart, close to the fence of the wheat field on the right-hand side. At the bottom of the fence-post, opposite the third tree, will be found a small pasteboard box.

The messenger will place the answer in this box and return immediately to Summit.

If you attempt any treachery or fail to comply with our demand as stated, you will never see your boy again.

If you pay the money as demanded, he will be returned to you safe and well within three hours. These terms are final, and if you do not accede to them no further communication will be attempted.

Two Desperate Men

I addressed this letter to Dorset, and put it in my pocket. As I was about to start, the kid comes up to me and says:

"Aw, Snake-eye, you said I could play the Black Scout while you was gone."

"Play it, of course," says I. "Mr. Bill will play with you. What kind of a game is it?"

"I'm the Black Scout," says Red Chief, "and I have to ride to the stockade to warn the settlers that the Indians are coming. I'm tired of playing Indian myself. I want to be the Black Scout."

"All right," says I. "It sounds harmless to me. I guess Mr. Bill will help you foil the pesky savages."

"What am I to do?" asks Bill, looking at the kid suspiciously.

"You are the hoss," says Black Scout. "Get down on your hands and knees. How can I ride to the stockade without a hoss?"

"You'd better keep him interested," said I, "till we get the scheme going. Loosen up."

Bill gets down on his all fours, and a look comes in his eye like a rabbit's when you catch it in a trap.

"How far is it to the stockade, kid?" he asks, in a husky manner of voice.

"Ninety miles," says the Black Scout. "And you have to hump yourself to get there on time. Whoa, now!"

The Black Scout jumps on Bill's back and digs his heels in his side.

"For Heaven's sake," says Bill, "hurry back, Sam, as soon as you can. I wish we hadn't made the ransom more than a thousand. Say, you quit kicking me or I'll get up and warm you good."

I walked over to Poplar Grove and sat around the post office and store, talking with the chaw-bacons that came in to trade. One whiskerando says that he hears Summit is all upset on account of Elder Ebenezer Dorset's boy having been lost or stolen. That was all I wanted to know. I bought some smoking tobacco, referred casually to the price of black-eyed peas, posted my letter surreptitiously, and came away. The postmaster said the mail carrier would come by in an hour to take the mail to Summit.

When I got back to the cave Bill and the boy were not to be found. I explored the vicinity of the cave, and risked a yodel or two, but there was no response.

So I lighted my pipe and sat down on a mossy bank to await developments.

In about half an hour I heard the bushes rustle, and Bill wabbled out into the little glade in front of the cave. Behind him was the kid, stepping softly like a scout, with a broad grin on his face. Bill stopped, took off his hat, and wiped his face with a red handkerchief. The kid stopped about eight feet behind him.

"Sam," says Bill, "I suppose you'll think I'm a renegade, but I couldn't help it. I'm a grown person with masculine proclivities and habits of self-defense, but there is a time when all systems of egotism and predominance fail. The boy is gone. I sent him home. All is off. There was martyrs in old times," goes on

Bill, "that suffered death rather than give up the particular graft they enjoyed. None of 'em ever was subjugated to such supernatural tortures as I have been. I tried to be faithful to our articles of depredation; but there came a limit."

"What's the trouble, Bill?" I asks him.

"I was rode," says Bill, "the ninety miles to the stockade, not barring an inch. Then, when the settlers was rescued, I was given oats. Sand ain't a palatable substitute. And then; for an hour I had to try to explain to him why there was nothin' in holes, how a road can run both ways, and what makes the grass green. I tell you, Sam, a human can only stand so much. I takes him by the neck of his clothes and drags him down the mountain. On the way he kicks my legs black and blue from the knees down; and I've got to have two or three bites on my thumb and hand cauterized.

"But he's gone"—continues Bill—"gone home. I showed him the road to Summit and kicked him about eight feet nearer there at one kick. I'm sorry we lose the ransom; but it was either that or Bill Driscoll to the madhouse."

Bill is puffing and blowing, but there is a look of ineffable peace and growing content on his rose-pink features.

"Bill," says I, "there isn't any heart disease in your family, is there?"

"No," says Bill, "nothing chronic except malaria and accidents. Why?"

"Then you might turn around," says I, "and have a look behind you."

Bill turns and sees the boy, and loses his complexion and sits down plump on the ground and begins to pluck aimlessly at grass and little sticks. For an hour I was afraid of his mind. And then I told him that my scheme was to put the whole job through immediately and that we would get the ransom and be off with it by midnight if old Dorset fell in with our proposition.

So Bill braced up enough to give the kid a weak sort of a smile and a promise to play the Russian in a Japanese war with him as soon as he felt a little better.

I had a scheme for collecting that ransom without danger of being caught by counterplots that ought to commend itself to professional kidnappers. The tree under which the answer was to be left—and the money later on—was close to the road fence with big, bare fields on all sides. If a gang of constables should be watching for anyone to come for the note, they could see him a long way off crossing the fields or in the road. But no, sirree! At half-past eight I was up in that tree as well hidden as a tree toad, waiting for the messenger to arrive.

Exactly on time, a half-grown boy rides up the road on a bicycle, locates the pasteboard box at the foot of the fence-post, slips a folded piece of paper into it, and pedals away again back toward Summit.

I waited an hour and then concluded the thing was square. I slid down the tree, got the note, slipped along the fence till I struck the woods, and was back at the cave in another half an hour. I opened the note, got near the lantern, and read it to Bill. It was written with a pen in a crabbed hand, and the sum and substance of it was this:

Two Desperate Men.

Gentlemen: I received your letter today by post, in regard to the ransom you ask for the return of my son. I think you are a little high in your demands, and I hereby make you a counter-proposition, which I am inclined to believe you will accept. You bring Johnny home and pay me two hundred and fifty dollars in cash, and I agree to take him off your hands. You had better come at night, for the neighbors believe he is lost, and I couldn't be responsible for what they would do to anybody they saw bringing him back. Very respectfully,

Ebenezer Dorset

"Great pirates of Penzance," says I; "of all the impudent—"

But I glanced at Bill, and hesitated. He had the most appealing look in his eyes I ever saw on the face of a dumb or a talking brute.

"Sam," says he, "what's two hundred and fifty dollars, after all? We've got the money. One more night of this kid will send me to a bed in Bedlam. Besides being a thorough gentleman, I think Mr. Dorset is a spendthrift for making us such a liberal offer. You ain't going to let the chance go, are you?"

"Tell you the truth, Bill," says I, "this little he ewe lamb has somewhat got on my nerves too. We'll take him home, pay the ransom, and make our getaway."

We took him home that night. We got him to go by telling him that his father had bought a silver-mounted rifle and a pair of moccasins for him, and we were to hunt bears the next day.

It was just twelve o'clock when we knocked at Ebenezer's front door. Just at the moment when I should have been abstracting the fifteen hundred dollars from the box under the tree, according to the original proposition, Bill was counting out two hundred and fifty dollars into Dorset's hand.

When the kid found out we were going to leave him at home he started up a howl like a calliope and fastened himself as tight as a leech to Bill's leg. His father peeled him away gradually, like a porous plaster.

"How long can you hold him?" asks Bill.

"I'm not as strong as I used to be," says old Dorset, "but I think I can promise you ten minutes."

"Enough," says Bill. "In ten minutes I shall cross the Central, Southern, and Middle Western States, and be legging it trippingly for the Canadian border."

And, as dark as it was, and as fat as Bill was, and as good a runner as I am, he was a good mile and a half out of Summit before I could catch up with him.

Finley P. Dunne
[1867–1936]

One of our early urban humorists, Finley P. Dunne was a brilliant journalist who quickly climbed the ladder of Chicago's leading newspapers. Dunne's deep contempt for injustice and hypocrisy led to the creation of Martin Dooley. Dooley first appeared in August 1893 in the *Chicago Evening Post* and was soon syndicated, to the delight of the public. A saloonkeeper, historian, social observer, economist, and philosopher, Dooley is the product of Dunne's middle-class Irish-American upbringing. In his Irish dialect, Dooley could get away with statements that would be outright libel for Dunne, the reporter, to write. His shrewd political insight, keen sense of social justice, and sound philosophy are revealed through witty and wise observations on the American public scene.

THE BIG FINE

"That was a splendid fine they soaked Jawn D. with," said Mr. Dooley.

"What did they give him?" asked Mr. Hennessy.

"Twenty-nine millyon dollars," said Mr. Dooley.

"Oh, great!" said Mr. Hennessy. "That's a grand fine. It's a gorjous fine. I can't hardly believe it."

"It's thrue, though," said Mr. Dooley. "Twinty-nine millyon dollars. Divvle th' cent less. I can't exactly make out what th' charge was that they arrested him on, but th' gin'ral idee is that Jawn D. was goin' around loaded up to th' guards with Standard Ile, exceedin' th' speed limit in acquirin' money, an' singin' 'A charge to keep I have' till th' neighbors cud stand it no longer. The judge says: 'Ye're an old offender an' I'll have to make an example iv ye. Twenty-nine millyon dollars or fifty-eight millyon days. Call th' next case, Misther Clerk.

"Did he pay th' fine? He did not. Iv coorse he cud if he wanted to. He wuddent have to pawn annything to get th' money, ye can bet on that. All he'd have to do would be to put his hand down in his pocket, skin twenty-nine millyon dollar bills off iv his roll an' hurl thim at th' clerk. But he refused to pay as a matter iv principle. 'Twas not that he needed th' money. He don't care f'r money in th' passionate way that you an' me do, Hinnissy. Th' likes iv us are as crazy about a dollar as a man is about his child whin he has on'y wan. Th' chances are we'll spoil it. But Jawn D., havin' a large an' growin' fam'ly iv dollars, takes on'y a kind iv gin'ral inthrest in thim. He's issued a statement

78

sayin' that he's a custojeen iv money appinted be himsilf. He looks afther his own money an' th' money iv other people. He takes it an' puts it where it won't hurt thim an' they won't spoil it. He's a kind iv a society f'r th' previntion of croolty to money. If he finds a man misusing his money he takes it away fr'm him an' adopts it. Ivry Saturdah night he lets th' man see it f'r a few hours. An' he says he's surprised to find that whin, with th' purest intintions in th' wurruld, he is found thryin' to coax our little money to his home where it'll find conjanial surroundings an' have other money to play with, th' people thry to lynch him an' th' polis arrest him f'r abduction.

"So as a matther iv principle he appealed th' case. An appeal, Hinnissy, is where ye ask wan coort to show its contempt f'r another coort. 'Tis sthrange that all th' pathrites that have wanted to hang Willum Jennings Bryan an' mesilf f'r not showin' proper respect f'r th' joodicyary, are now showin' their respect f'r th' joodicyary be appealin' fr'm their decisions. Ye'd think Jawn D. wud bow his head reverentially in th' awful presence iv Kenesaw Mt. Landis an' sob out: 'Thank ye'er honor. This here noble fine fills me with joy. But d'ye think ye give me enough? If agreeable I'd like to make it an even thirty millyons.' But he doesn't. He's like mesilf. Him an' me bows to th' decisions iv th' coorts on'y if they bow first.

"I have gr-reat respect f'r th' joodicyary, as fine a lot iv cross an' indignant men as ye'll find annywhere. I have th' same respect f'r thim as they have f'r each other. But I niver bow to a decision iv a judge onless, first, it's pleasant to me, an', second, other judges bow to it. Ye can't be too careful about what decisions ye bow to. A decision that seems agreeable may turn out like an acquaintance ye scrape up at a picnic. Ye may be ashamed iv it to-morrah. Manny's th' time I've bowed to a decree iv a coort on'y to see it go up gaily to th' supreem coort, knock at th' dure an' be kicked down stairs be an angry old gintleman in a black silk petticoat. A decree iv th' coort has got to be pretty vinrable befure I do more thin greet it with a pleasant smile.

"Me idee was whin I read about Jawn D.'s fine that he'd settle at wanst, payin' twenty-eight millyon dollars in millyon dollar bills an' th' other millyon in chicken-feed like ten thousand dollar bills just to annoy th' clerk. But I ought to've known betther. Manny's th' time I've bent me proud neck to a decision iv a coort that lasted no longer thin it took th' lawyer f'r th' definse to call up another judge on th' tillyphone. A judge listens to a case f'r days an' hears, while he's figurin' a possible goluf score on his blotting pad, th' argymints iv two or three lawyers that no wan wud dare to offer a judgeship to. Gin'rally speakin', judges are lawyers. They get to be judges because they have what Hogan calls th' joodicyal timp'ramint, which is why annybody gets a job. Th' other kind people won't take a job. They'd rather take a chance. Th' judge listens to a case f'r days an' decides it th' way he intinded to. D'ye find th' larned counsel that's just been beat climbin' up on th' bench an' throwin' his arms around th' judge? Ye bet ye don't. He gathers his law books into his arms, gives th' magistrate a look that means, 'There's an eliction next year,' an' runs down th' hall to another judge. Th' other judge hears his kick an' says he: 'I don't know annything about this here case except what ye've whispered to me, but I know me larned collague an' I wuddent thrust him to referee a roller-skatin' contest. Don't pay th' fine till ye hear fr'm me.' Th' on'y wan that bows to th' decision is th' fellow that won, an' pretty soon he sees he's made a mistake, f'r wan day th' other coort comes out an' declares that th' decision of th' lower coort is another argymint in favor iv abolishing night law schools.

"That's th' way Jawn D. felt about it an' he didn't settle. I wondher will they put him away if he don't pay ivinchooly? 'Twill be a long sentence. A frind iv mine wanst got full iv kerosene an' attempted to juggle

a polisman. They thried him whin he come out iv th'
emergency hospital an' fined him a hundhred dollars.
He didn't happen to have that amount with him at th'
moment or at anny moment since th' day he was born.
But the judge was very lenient with him. He said he
needn't pay it if he cudden't. Th' coort wud give him
a letther of inthroduction to th' bridewell an' he cud
stay there f'r two hundhred days. At that rate it'll be
a long time befure Jawn D. an' me meet again on the
goluf-links. Hogan has it figured out that if Jawn D.
refuses to go back on his Puritan principles an' separate
himsilf fr'm his money he'll be wan hundhred an'
fifty-eight thousand years in cold storage. A man ought
to be pretty good at th' lock step in a hundhred an'
fifty-eight thousand years.

"Well, sir, glory be but times has changed whin they
land me gr-reat an' good frind with a fine that's about
akel to three millyon dhrunk an' disorderly cases.
'Twud've been cheaper if he'd took to dhrink arly in
life. I've made a vow, Hinnissy, niver to be very rich.
I'd like to be a little rich, but not rich enough f'r anny
wan to notice that me pockets bulged. Time was whin
I dhreamed iv havin' money an' lots iv it. 'Tis thrue
I begun me dhreams at th' wrong end, spent th' money
befure I got it. I was always clear about th' way to
spend it but oncertain about th' way to get it. If th'
Lord had intinded me to be a rich man He'd've turned
me dhreams around an' made me clear about makin'
th' money but very awkward an' shy about gettin' rid
iv it. There are two halves to ivry dollar. Wan is
knowin' how to make it an' th' other is not knowin'
how to spend it comfortably. Whin I hear iv a man
with gr-reat business capacity I know he's got an akel
amount iv spending incapacity. No matter how much
he knew about business he wuddent be rich if he wasn't
totally ignorant iv a science that we have developed as
far as our means will allow. But now, I tell ye, I don't
dhream iv bein' rich. I'm afraid iv it. In th' good old
days th' polis coorts were crowded with th' poor. They

weren't charged with poverty, iv coorse, but with the results iv poverty, d'ye mind. Now, be Hivens, th' rich have invaded even th' coorts an' the bridewell. Manny a face wearin' side whiskers an' gold-rimmed specs peers fr'm th' windows iv th' black Maria. 'What's this man charged with?' says th' coort. 'He was found in possession iv tin millyon dollars,' says th' polisman. An' th' judge puts on th' black cap."

"Well," said Mr. Hennessy, " 'tis time they got what was comin' to thim."

"I'll not say ye're wrong," said Mr. Dooley. "I see the way me frind Jawn D. feels about it. He thinks he's doin' a great sarvice to th' worruld collectin' all th' money in sight. It might remain in incompetint hands if he didn't get it. 'Twud be a shame to lave it where it'd be misthreated. But th' on'y throuble with Jawn is that he don't see how th' other fellow feels about it. As a father iv about thirty dollars I want to bring thim up mesilf in me own foolish way. I may not do what's right be thim. I may be too indulgent with thim. Their home life may not be happy. Perhaps 'tis clear that if they wint to th' Rockyfellar institution f'r th' care iv money they'd be in betther surroundings, but whin Jawn thries to carry thim off I raise a cry iv 'Polis,' a mob iv people that niver had a dollar iv their own an' never will have wan, pounce on th' misguided man, th' polis pinch him, an' th' governmint condemns th' institution an' lets out th' inmates an' a good manny iv thim go to th' bad."

"D'ye think he'll iver sarve out his fine?" asked Mr. Hennessy.

"I don't know," said Mr. Dooley. "But if if he does, whin he comes out at the end iv a hundhred an fifty-eight thousand years he'll find a great manny changes in men's hats an' th' means iv transportation but not much in annything else. He may find flyin' machines, though it'll be arly f'r thim, but he'll see a good manny people still walkin' to their wurruk."

Will Rogers
[1879–1935]

This shy humorist, who rose from twirling a
lasso in Wild West shows to twitting presidents
and royalty, is the very essence of American
common sense and plain good nature. Will
Rogers took great pride in the fact that he was
part American Indian. Born into a comfortable
and respected family, he preferred rope-
throwing to managing the family ranch. He
began his career on the vaudeville stage performing rope tricks interspersed with humorous
monologues on current events. He became one
of the star attractions of the Ziegfeld Follies and
appeared in motion pictures and on radio, as
well as writing a syndicated newspaper column
famous for its homespun humor, wholesome
philosophy, and sharp critcism of contemporary
politics. When he was killed with the famed
aviator Wiley Post in a plane crash in Alaska,
Rogers was mourned throughout the world.

RENO, NEVADA

You don't know what a Country we have got till you start prowling around it. Personally I like the small places and sparsely populated States. A place looks better before it gets houses on it than it does afterwards. I hit Nevada the other day. I was billed to play Reno, and say she sure is a pretty little town! Its a regular Oasis right there in the heart of the Sage Brush Country, got beautiful homes and Cottages and I am telling you its worth staying there a while to get rid of a lot of husbands that I know.

I had both eyes all cocked to get a peek at the "Divorcees." I was like the little dames from the east when they first visited Hollywood and are all eyes for the Movie Stars. Well I was all set to get a peek at the "Liberty hunters." You know I dident know it, and I bet you dident either (and thats why I have to do all this traveling around and finding out things for you and all you have to do is to stay at home and just learn what it has taken me so much bother to find out for you). Well, there is just as many men come to Reno for divorces as there is Women. So you see Women are not the only things that are dissatisfied with their mates. Some women are failures just as well as men. And you see when some woman comes there to uncouple from the "old grouch" and don't particularly have her mind made up about the next matrimonial accident why you see with all these men there on the same mission, Why she may pick up something worth while right there. The two sexes are just a-setting right there ready to console each other, and a lot of times you can get just as good or maybe better than you are throwing away right there in Reno. You see you got time to write back and investigate each others financial status. But its just a nice little city and outside of Divorces they got a River running through it and a little Zoo in a pretty park with two Buffalo. A mail and a Female and two elk, Male and Female. In fact pairs of several kind of animals and birds and reptiles. It looks like they mated 'em off that way just to show the "Industry" what can be accomplished if they had been born a reptile or animal instead of practically human. It looked to me like an ad against their business there in Reno, but I guess they know best. Lawyers meet the trains and line up and holler out the same as Porters do down South at depots for Hotels. They got Lawyers there that can get you loose from an Octopus. They can point out houses where some of the most famous husbands in the world were tied a can to. Lots of them buy these cottages and live in them till their probation is over and then maby sell them to some other "Irreconcible" or lots of them, they tell me, keep their houses there, and then use them when they come back on the next case. Some women have as many as four and five "notches" on the same house, showing they had got their Man.

CONGRESS

The way to judge a good Comedy is by how long it will last and have people talk about it. Now Congress has turned out some that have lived for years and people are still laughing about them.

Girls win a little State Popularity Contest that is conducted in some Newspaper; then they are put into the Movies to entertain 110 million people who they never saw or know anything about. Now that's the same way with the Capitol Comedy Company of Washington. They win a State Popularity Contest backed by a Newspaper and are sent to Washington to turn out Laws for 110 million people they never saw.

They have what they call Congress, or the Lower House. That compares to what we call the Scenario Department. That's where somebody gets the idea of what he thinks will make a good Comedy Bill or Law, and they argue around and put it into shape.

Then it is passed along, printed, or shot, or Photographed, as we call it; then it reaches the Senate or the Cutting and Titling Department. Now, in our Movie Studios we have what we call Gag Men whose sole business is to just furnish some little Gag, or Amendment as they call it, which will get a laugh or perhaps change the whole thing around.

Now the Senate has what is considered the best and highest priced Gag men that can be collected anywhere. Why, they put in so many little gags or amendments that the poor Author of the thing don't know his own story.

They consider if a man can sit there in the Studio in

Washington and just put in one funny amendment in each Bill, or production, that will change it from what it originally meant, why, he is considered to have earned his pay.

Now, Folks, why patronize California-made Productions? The Capitol Comedy Company of Washington, D.C., have never made a failure. They are every one, 100 percent funny, or 100 percent sad.

Dorothy Parker
[1893–1967]

Dorothy Parker zeros in on target with deadly aim. Although her attitude is flippant, her style is precise and polished. Born in New Jersey and educated at the Blessed Sacrament Convent in New York City, she began her literary career as a drama critic, earning a deserved reputation for ruthless reviews. She was associated with such leading magazines as *Vogue, Vanity Fair,* and *The New Yorker,* and during the 1920s was a member of the famed "Round Table," a group of leading writers and humorists who lunched regularly at the Algonquin Hotel. Later she lived in Hollywood for a number of years, collaborating on several film scenarios with only moderate success. Her poetry, short stories, and sketches demonstrate her particular gift for sophisticated satire and scathing irony —often with a bitter edge. "The humorist has never been happy, anyhow," Parker once commented.

ONE PERFECT ROSE

A single flow'r he sent me, since we met.
　All tenderly his messenger he chose;
Deep-hearted, pure, with scented dew still wet—
　One perfect rose.

I knew the language of the floweret;
　"My fragile leaves," it said, "his heart enclose."
Love long has taken for his amulet
　One perfect rose.

Why is it no one ever sent me yet
　One perfect limousine, do you suppose?
Ah no, it's always just my luck to get
One perfect rose.

RÉSUMÉ

Razors pain you;
Rivers are damp;
Acids stain you;
And drugs cause cramp.
Guns aren't lawful;
Nooses give;
Gas smells awful;
You might as well live.

JUST A LITTLE ONE

I like this place, Fred. This is a nice place. How did you ever find it? I think you're perfectly marvelous, discovering a speakeasy in the year 1928. And they let you right in, without asking you a single question. I bet you could get into the subway without using anybody's name. Couldn't you, Fred?

Oh, I like this place better and better, now that my eyes are getting accustomed to it. You mustn't let them tell you this lighting system is original with them, Fred; they got the idea from the Mammoth Cave. This is you sitting next to me, isn't it? Oh, you can't fool me. I'd know that knee anywhere.

You know what I like about this place? It's got atmosphere. That's what it's got. If you would ask the waiter to bring a fairly sharp knife, I could cut off a nice little block of the atmosphere, to take home with me. It would be interesting to have for my memory book. I'm going to start keeping a memory book tomorrow. Don't let me forget.

Why, I don't know, Fred—what are you going to have? Then I guess I'll have a highball, too; please, just a little one. Is it really real Scotch? Well, that will be a new experience for me. You ought to see the Scotch I've got home in my cupboard; at least it was in the cupboard this morning—it's probably eaten its way out by now. I got it for my birthday. Well, it was something. The birthday before, all I got was a year older.

This is a nice highball, isn't it? Well, well, well, to think of me having real Scotch; I'm out of the bush leagues at last. Are you going to have another one?

Well, I shouldn't like to see you drinking all by yourself, Fred. Solitary drinking is what causes half the crime in the country. That's what's responsible for the failure of Prohibition. But please, Fred, tell him to make mine just a little one. Make it awfully weak; just cambric Scotch.

It will be nice to see the effect of veritable whisky upon one who has been accustomed only to the simpler forms of entertainment. You'll like that, Fred. You'll stay by me if anything happens, won't you? I don't think there will be anything spectacular, but I want to ask you one thing, just in case. Don't let me take any horses home with me. It doesn't matter so much about stray dogs and kittens, but elevator boys get awfully stuffy when you try to bring in a horse. You might just as well know that about me now, Fred. You can always tell that the crash is coming when I start getting tender about Our Dumb Friends. Three highballs, and I think I'm St. Francis of Assisi.

But I don't believe anything is going to happen to me on these. That's because they're made of real stuff. That's what the difference is. This just makes you feel fine. Oh, I feel swell, Fred. You do too, don't you? I knew you did, because you look better. I love that tie you have on. Oh, did Edith give it to you? Ah, wasn't that nice of her? You know, Fred, most people are really awfully nice. There are darn few that aren't pretty fine at heart. You've got a beautiful heart, Fred. You'd be the first person I'd go to if I were in trouble. I guess you are just about the best friend I've got in the world. But I worry about you, Fred. I do so, too. I don't think you take enough care of yourself. You ought to take care of yourself for your friends' sake. You oughtn't to drink all this terrible stuff that's around; you owe it to your friends to be careful. You don't mind my talking to you like this, do you? You see, dear, it's because I'm your friend that I hate to see you not taking care of yourself. It hurts me to see you batting around the way you've been doing. You ought to stick to this place, where they have real Scotch that can't do you any harm. Oh, darling, do you really think I ought to? Well, you tell him just a little bit of a one. Tell him, sweet.

Do you come here often, Fred? I shouldn't worry about you so much if I knew you were in a safe place like this. Oh, is this where you were Thursday night? I see. Why, no, it didn't make a bit of difference, only you told me to call you up, and like a fool I broke a date I had, just because I thought I was going to see you. I just sort of naturally thought so, when you said to call you up. Oh, good Lord, don't make all that fuss about it. It really didn't make the slightest difference. It just didn't seem a very friendly way to behave, that's all. I don't know—I'd been believing we were such good friends. I'm an awful idiot about people, Fred. There aren't many who are really your friend at heart. Practically anybody would play you dirt for a nickel. Oh, yes, they would.

Was Edith here with you, Thursday night? This place must be very becoming to her. Next to being in a coal mine, I can't think of anywhere she could go that the light would be more flattering to that pan of hers. Do you really know a lot of people that say she's good-looking? You must have a wide acquaintance among the astigmatic, haven't you, Freddie, dear? Why, and you look great, too. I'm proud to have you for a friend. Do you realize, Fred, what a rare thing a friend is, when you think of all the terrible people there are in this world? Animals are much better than people. God, I love animals. That's what I like about you, Fred. You're so fond of animals.

Look, I'll tell you what let's do, after we've had just a little highball. Let's go out and pick up a lot of stray dogs. I never had enough dogs in my life, did you? We ought to have more dogs. And maybe there'd be some cats around, if we looked. And a horse, I've never had one single horse, Fred. Isn't that rotten? Not one single horse. Ah, I'd like a nice old cab-horse, Fred. Wouldn't you? I'd like to take care of it and comb its hair and everything. Ah, don't be stuffy about it, Fred, please don't. I need a horse, honestly I do. Wouldn't you like one? It would be so sweet and kind. Let's have a drink and then let's you and I go out and get a horsie, Freddie—just a little one, darling, just a little one.

James Thurber
[1894–1961]

Comic artist James Thurber was born in Columbus, Ohio and studied at Ohio State. After working as a newspaper reporter for several years, he joined *The New Yorker* in 1927, a warm affiliation which would last his lifetime. Thurber's essays, sketches, fables, parables, and stories are peopled with remarkable beings—both human and animal. They are frequently illustrated with clear, fluid, cartoon-like drawings which happily enmesh with the prose. The prose itself is simple and matter-of-fact, suggesting an openness and calm that belie—and emphasize—the underlying chaos and mayhem of his situations. After the age of forty, Thurber became progressively blind, but he continued to write and illustrate for many more years.

THE RABBITS WHO CAUSED
ALL THE TROUBLE

Within the memory of the youngest child there was a family of rabbits who lived near a pack of wolves. The wolves announced that they did not like the way the rabbits were living. (The wolves were crazy about the way they themselves were living, because it was the only way to live.) One night several wolves were killed in an earthquake and this was blamed on the rabbits, for it is well known that rabbits pound on the ground with their hind legs and cause earthquakes. On another night one of the wolves was killed by a bolt of lightning and this was also blamed on the rabbits, for it is well known that lettuce-eaters cause lightning. The wolves threatened to civilize the rabbits if they didn't behave, and the rabbits decided to run away to a desert island. But the other animals, who lived at a great distance, shamed them, saying, "You must stay where you are and be brave. This is no world for escapists. If the wolves attack you, we will come to your aid, in all probability." So the rabbits continued to live near the wolves and one day there was a terrible flood which drowned a great many wolves. This was blamed on the rabbits, for it is well known that carrot-nibblers with long ears cause floods. The wolves descended on the rabbits, for their own good, and imprisoned them in a dark cave, for their own protection.

When nothing was heard about the rabbits for some weeks, the other animals demanded to know what had happened to them. The wolves replied that the rabbits had been eaten and since they had been eaten the affair was a purely internal matter. But the other animals warned that they might possibly unite against the wolves unless some reason was given for the destruction of the rabbits. So the wolves gave them one. "They were trying to escape," said the wolves, "and, as you know, this is no world for escapists."

Moral: Run, don't walk, to the nearest desert island.

THE HEN AND THE HEAVENS

Once upon a time a little red hen was picking up stones and worms and seeds in a barnyard when something fell on her head. "The heavens are falling down!" she shouted, and she began to run, still shouting, "The heavens are falling down!" All the hens that she met and all the roosters and turkeys and ducks laughed at her, smugly, the way you laugh at one who is terrified when you aren't. "What did you say?" they chortled. "The heavens are falling down!" cried the little red hen. Finally a very pompous rooster said to her, "Don't be silly, my dear, it was only a pea that fell on your head." And he laughed and laughed and everybody else except the little red hen laughed. Then suddenly with an awful roar great chunks of crystallized cloud and huge blocks of icy blue sky began to drop on everybody from above, and everybody was killed, the laughing rooster and the little red hen and everybody else in the barnyard, for the heavens actually *were* falling down.

Moral: It wouldn't surprise me a bit if they did.

THE UNICORN IN THE GARDEN

Once upon a sunny morning a man who sat in a breakfast nook looked up from his scrambled eggs to see a white unicorn with a gold horn quietly cropping the roses in the garden. The man went up to the bedroom where his wife was still asleep and woke her. "There's a unicorn in the garden," he said. "Eating roses." She opened one unfriendly eye and looked at him. "The unicorn is a mythical beast," she said, and turned her back on him. The man walked slowly downstairs and out into the garden. The unicorn was still there; he was now browsing among the tulips. "Here, unicorn," said the man, and he pulled up a lily and gave it to him. The unicorn ate it gravely. With a high heart, because there was a unicorn in his garden, the man went upstairs and roused his wife again. "The unicorn," he said, "ate a lily." His wife sat up in bed and looked at him, coldly. "You are a booby," she said, "and I am going to have you put in the booby-hatch." The man, who had never liked the words "booby" and "booby-hatch," and who liked them even less on a shining morning when there was a unicorn in the garden, thought for a moment. "We'll see about that," he said He walked over to the door. "He has a golden horn in the middle of his forehead," he told her. Then he went back to the garden to watch the unicorn; but the unicorn had gone away. The man sat down among the roses and went to sleep.

As soon as the husband had gone out of the house, the wife got up and dressed as fast as she could. She was very excited and there was a gloat in her eye. She telephoned the police and she telephoned a psychiatrist; she told them to hurry to her house and bring a straitjacket. When the police and the psychiatrist arrived they sat down in chairs and looked at her, with great interest. "My husband," she said, "saw a unicorn this morning." The police looked at the psychiatrist and the psychiatrist looked at the police. "He told me it ate a lily," she said. The psychiatrist looked at the police and the police looked at the psychiatrist. "He told me it had a golden horn in the middle of its forehead," she said. At a solemn signal from the psychiatrist, the police leaped from their chairs and seized the wife. They had a hard time subduing her, for she put up a terrific struggle, but they finally subdued her. Just as they got her into the straitjacket, the husband came back into the house.

"Did you tell your wife you saw a unicorn?" asked the police. "Of course not," said the husband. "The unicorn is a mythical beast." "That's all I wanted to know," said the psychiatrist. "Take her away. I'm sorry, sir, but your wife is as crazy as a jay bird." So they took her away, cursing and screaming, and shut her up in an institution. The husband lived happily ever after.

Moral: Don't count your boobies until they are hatched.

THE NIGHT
THE GHOST GOT IN

The ghost that got into our house on the night of November 17, 1915, raised such a hullabaloo of misunderstandings that I am sorry I didn't just let it keep on walking, and go to bed. Its advent caused my mother to throw a shoe through a window of the house next door and ended up with my grandfather shooting a patrolman. I am sorry, therefore, as I have said, that I ever paid any attention to the footsteps.

They began about a quarter past one o'clock in the morning, a rhythmic, quick-cadenced walking around the dining-room table. My mother was asleep in one room upstairs, my brother Herman in another; grandfather was in the attic, in the old walnut bed which, as you will remember, once fell on my father. I had just stepped out of the bathtub and was busily rubbing myself with a towel when I heard the steps. They were the steps of a man walking rapidly around the dining-room table downstairs. The light from the bathroom shone down the back steps, which dropped directly into the dining room; I could see the faint shine of plates on the plate-rail; I couldn't see the table. The steps kept going round and round the table; at regular intervals a board creaked, when it was trod upon. I supposed at first that it was my father or my brother Roy, who had gone to Indianapolis but were expected home at any time. I suspected next that it was a burglar. It did not enter my mind until later that it was a ghost.

After the walking had gone on for perhaps three

minutes, I tiptoed to Herman's room. "Psst!" I hissed, in the dark, shaking him. "Awp," he said, in the low, hopeless tone of a despondent beagle—he always half suspected that something would "get him" in the night. I told him who I was. "There's something downstairs!" I said. He got up and followed me to the head of the back staircase. We listened together. There was no sound. The steps had ceased. Herman looked at me in some alarm: I had only the bath towel around my waist. He wanted to go back to bed, but I gripped his arm. "There's something down there!" I said. Instantly the steps began again, circled the dining-room table like a man running, and started up the stairs toward us, heavily, two at a time. The light still shone palely down the stairs; we saw nothing coming; we only heard the steps. Herman rushed to his room and slammed the door. I slammed shut the door at the stairs top and held my knee against it. After a long minute, I slowly opened it again. There was nothing there. There was no sound. None of us ever heard the ghost again.

The slamming of the doors had aroused Mother: she peered out of her room. "What on earth are you boys doing?" she demanded. Herman ventured out of his room. "Nothing," he said, gruffly, but he was, in color, a light green. "What was all that running around downstairs?" said Mother. So she had heard the steps, too! We just looked at her. "Burglars!" she shouted intuitively. I tried to quiet her by starting lightly downstairs.

"Come on, Herman," I said.

"I'll stay with Mother," he said. "She's all excited."

I stepped back onto the landing.

"Don't either of you go a step," said Mother. "We'll call the police." Since the phone was downstairs, I didn't see how we were going to call the police—nor did I want the police—but Mother made one of her quick, incomparable decisions. She flung up a window of her bedroom which faced the bedroom windows of the house of a neighbor, picked up a shoe, and whammed it through a pane of glass across the narrow space that separated the two houses. Glass tinkled into the bedroom occupied by a retired engraver named Bodwell and his wife. Bodwell had been for some years in rather a bad way and was subject to mild "attacks." Most everybody we knew or lived near had *some* kind of attacks.

It was now about two o'clock of a moonless night; clouds hung black and low. Bodwell was at the window in a minute, shouting, frothing a little, shaking his fist. "We'll sell the house and go back to Peoria," we could hear Mrs. Bodwell saying. It was some time before Mother "got through" to Bodwell. "Burglars!" she shouted. "Burglars in the house!" Herman and I hadn't dared to tell her that it was not burglars but ghosts, for she was even more afraid of ghosts than of burglars. Bodwell at first thought that she meant there were burglars in his house, but finally he quieted down and called the police for us over an extension phone by his bed. After he had disappeared from the window, Mother suddenly made as if to throw another shoe, not because there was further need of it but, as she later explained, because the thrill of heaving a shoe through a window glass had enormously taken her fancy. I prevented her.

The police were on hand in a commendably short time: a Ford sedan full of them, two on motorcycles, and a patrol wagon with about eight in it and a few reporters. They began banging at our front door. Flashlights shot streaks of gleam up and down the walls, across the yard, down the walk between our house and Bodwell's. "Open up!" cried a hoarse voice. "We're men from Headquarters!" I wanted to go down and let them in, since there they were, but Mother wouldn't hear of it. "You haven't a stitch on," she pointed out. "You'd catch your death." I wound the towel around me again. Finally the cops put their shoulders to our big heavy front door with its thick beveled glass and broke it in: I could hear a rending of wood and a splash of glass on the floor of the hall. Their lights played all over the living room and crisscrossed nervously in the dining room, stabbed into hallways, shot up the front stairs and finally up the back. They caught me standing in my towel at the top. A heavy policeman bounded up the steps. "Who are you?" he demanded. "I live here," I said. "Well, whattsa matta, ya hot?" he asked. It was, as a matter of fact, cold; I went to my room and pulled on some trousers. On my way out, a cop stuck a gun into my ribs. "Whatta you doin' here?" he demanded. "I live here," I said.

The officer in charge reported to Mother. "No sign of nobody, lady," he said. "Musta got away—whatt'd he look like?" "There were two or three of them," Mother said, "whooping and carrying on and slamming doors." "Funny," said the cop. "All ya windows and doors was locked on the inside tight as a tick."

Downstairs, we could hear the tromping of the other police. Police were all over the place; doors were yanked open, drawers were yanked open, windows were shot up and pulled down, furniture fell with dull thumps. A half-dozen policemen emerged out of the darkness of the front hallway upstairs. They began to ransack the floor: pulled beds away from walls, tore clothes off hooks in the closets, pulled suitcases and boxes off shelves. One of them found an old zither that Roy had won in a pool tournament. "Looky here, Joe," he said, strumming it with a big paw. The cop named Joe took it and turned it over. "What is it?" he asked me. "It's an old zither our guinea pig used to sleep on," I said. It was true that a pet guinea pig we once had would never sleep anywhere except on the zither, but I should never have said so. Joe and the other cop looked at me a long time. They put the zither back on a shelf.

"No sign o' nuthin'," said the cop who had first spoken to Mother. "This guy," he explained to the others, jerking a thumb at me, "was nekked. The lady seems historical." They all nodded, but said nothing;

just looked at me. In the small silence we all heard a creaking in the attic. Grandfather was turning over in bed. "What's 'at?" snapped Joe. Five or six cops sprang for the attic door before I could intervene or explain. I realized that it would be bad if they burst in on Grandfather unannounced, or even announced. He was going through a phase in which he believed that General Meade's men, under steady hammering by Stonewall Jackson, were beginning to retreat and even desert.

When I got to the attic, things were pretty confused. Grandfather had evidently jumped to the conclusion that the police were deserters from Meade's army, trying to hide away in his attic. He bounded out of bed wearing a long flannel nightgown over long woolen underwear, a nightcap, and a leather jacket around his chest. The cops must have realized at once that the indignant white-haired old man belonged in the house, but they had no chance to say so. "Back, ye cowardly dogs!" roared Grandfather. "Back t' the lines, ye goddam lily-livered cattle!" With that, he fetched the officer who found the zither a flat-handed smack alongside his head that sent him sprawling. The others beat a retreat, but not fast enough; Grandfather grabbed Zither's gun from its holster and let fly. The report seemed to crack the rafters; smoke filled the attic. A cop cursed and shot his hand to his shoulder. Somehow, we all finally got downstairs again and locked the door against the old gentleman. He fired once or twice more in the darkness and then went back to bed. "That was Grandfather," I explained to Joe, out of breath. "He thinks you're deserters." "I'll say he does," said Joe.

The cops were reluctant to leave without getting their hands on somebody besides Grandfather; the night had been distinctly a defeat for them. Furthermore, they obviously didn't like the "layout," something looked—and I can see their viewpoint—phony. They began to poke into things again. A reporter, a thin-

faced, wispy man, came up to me. I had put on one of
mother's blouses, not being able to find anything else.
The reporter looked at me with mingled suspicion and
interest. "Just what the hell is the real lowdown here,
Bud?" he asked. I decided to be frank with him. "We
had ghosts," I said. He gazed at me a long time as if
I were a slot machine into which he had, without
results, dropped a nickel. Then he walked away. The
cops followed him, the one Grandfather shot holding
his now-bandaged arm, cursing and blaspheming. "I'm
gonna get my gun back from that old bird," said the
zither-cop. "Yeh," said Joe. "You—and who else?" I
told them I would bring it to the stationhouse the
next day.

"What was the matter with that one policeman?"
Mother asked, after they had gone. "Grandfather shot
him," I said. "What for?" she demanded. I told her
he was a deserter. "Of all things!" said Mother. "He
was such a nice-looking young man."

Grandfather was fresh as a daisy and full of jokes at
breakfast next morning. We thought at first he had
forgotten all about what had happened, but he hadn't.
Over his third cup of coffee, he glared at Herman and
me. "What was the idee of all them cops tarryhootin'
round the house last night?" he demanded. He had us
there.

E. B. White
[1899–   ]

E. B. White, one of the most versatile American humorists, has produced a wealth of poems, editorials, essays, stories, sketches, and children's books. He was born in Mr. Vernon, New York, and during his childhood spent summers in Maine, where he later settled to farm and write. After graduation from Cornell University, White worked as a newspaper reporter and freelance writer. For many years he was affiliated with *The New Yorker* as columnist, editor, and contributor, and he also wrote regularly for *Harper's Magazine*. White is noted for his simple, beautiful prose and easy, informal style. His comments on contemporary culture reflect a love of nature and of privacy, the satisfactions of a simple life, and a gentle but strong defense of basic human values.

ABOUT MYSELF

I am a man of medium height. I keep my records in a Weis Folder Re-order Number 8003. The unpaid balance of my estimated tax for the year 1945 is item 3 less the sum of items 4 and 5. My eyes are gray. My Selective Service order number is 10789. The serial number is T1654. I am in Class IV-A, and have been variously in Class 3-A, Class I-A(H), and Clas 4-H. My social security number is 067-01-9841. I am married to U.S. Woman Number 067-01-9807. Her eyes are gray. This is not a joint declaration, nor is it made by an agent; therefore it need be signed only by me—and, as I said, I am a man of medium height.

I am the holder of a quit-claim deed recorded in Book 682, Page 501, in the county where I live. I hold Fire Insurance Policy Number 424747, continuing until the 23 day of October in the year nineteen hundred forty-five, at noon, and it is important that the written portions of all policies covering the same property read exactly alike. My cervical spine shows relatively good alignment with evidence of proliferative changes about the bodies consistent with early arthritis. (Essential clinical data: pain in neck radiating to mastoids and occipito-temporal region, not constant, moderately severe; patient in good general health and working.) My operator's license is Number 16200. It expired December 31, 1943, more than a year ago, but I am still carrying it and it appears to be serving the purpose. I shall renew it when I get time. I have made, published, and declared my last will and testament, and it thereby revokes all other wills and codicils at any time hereto-

fore made by me. I hold Basic A Mileage Ration
108950, O.P.A. Form R-525-C. The number of my car
is 18-388. Tickets A-14 are valid through March 21st.

I was born in District Number 5903, New York State.
My birth is registered in Volume 3/58 of the Department of Health. My father was a man of medium
height. His telephone number was 484. My mother was
a housewife. Her eyes were blue. Neither parent had
a social security number and neither was secure socially.
They drove to the depot behind an unnumbered horse.

I hold Individual Certificate Number 4320-209 with
the Equitable Life Assurance Society, in which a
corporation hereinafter called the employer has con-
tracted to insure my life for the sum of two thousand
dollars. My left front tire is Number 48KE8846, my
right front tire is Number 63T6895. My rear tires are,
from left to right, Number 6N4M5384 and Number
A26E5806D. I brush my hair with Whiting-Adams
Brush Number 010 and comb my hair with Pro-Phy-Lac-
Tic Comb Number 1201. My shaving brush is sterilized.
I take Pill Number 43934 after each meal and I can get
more of them by calling ELdorado 5-6770. I spray my
nose with De Vilbiss Atomizer Number 14. Sometimes
I stop the pain with Squibb Pill, Control Number
3K49979 (asprin). My wife (Number 067-01-9807)
takes Pill Number 49345.

I hold War Ration Book 40289EW, from which
have been torn Airplane Stamps Numbers 1, 2, and 3.
I also hold Book 159378CD, from which have been
torn Spare Number 2, Spare Number 37, and certain
other coupons. My wife holds Book 40288EW and
Book 159374CD. In accepting them, she recognized
that they remained the property of the United States
Government.

I have a black dog with cheeks of tan. Her number
is 11032. It is an old number. I shall renew it when I
get time. The analysis of her prepared food is guaran-
teed and is Case Number 1312. The ingredients are:
Cereal Flaked feeds (from Corn, Rice, Bran, and

Wheat), Meat Meal, Fish Liver and Glandular Meal, Soybean Oil Meal, Wheat Bran, Corn Germ Meal, 5% Kel-Centrate [containing Dried Skim Milk, Dehydrated Cheese, Vitamin B₁ (Thiamin), Flavin Concentrate, Carotene, Yeast, Vitamin A and D Feeding Oil (containing 3,000 U.S.P. units Vitamin A and 400 U.S.P. units Vitamin D per gram), Diastase (Enzyme), Wheat Germ Meal, Rice Polish Extract], 1½% Calcium Carbonate, .00037% Potassium Iodide, and ¼% Salt. She prefers offal.

When I finish what I am now writing it will be late in the day. It will be about half past five. I will then take up Purchase Order Number 245-9077-B-Final, which I received this morning from the Office of War Information and which covers the use of certain material they want to translate into a foreign language. Attached to the order are Standard Form Number 1034 (white) and three copies of Standard Form Number 1034a (yellow), also "Instructions for Preparation of Voucher by Vendor and Example of Prepared Voucher." The Appropriation Symbol of the Purchase Order is 1153700.001-501. The requisition number is B-827. The allotment is X5-207.1-R2-11. Voucher shall be prepared in ink, indelible pencil, or typewriter. For a while I will be vendor preparing voucher. Later on, when my head gets bad and the pain radiates, I will be voucher preparing vendor. I see that there is a list of twenty-one instructions which I will be following. Number One on the list is: "Name of payor agency as shown in the block 'appropriation symbol and title' in the upper left-hand corner of the Purchase Order." Number Five on the list is: "Vendor's personal account or invoice number," but whether that means Order Number 245-9077-B-Final, or Requisition B-827, or Allotment X5-207.1-R2-11, or Appropriation Symbol 1153700.001-501, I do not know, nor will I know later on in the evening after several hours of meditation, nor will I be able to find out by consulting Woman 067-01-9807, who is no better at filling out forms than

I am, nor after taking Pill Number 43934, which tends merely to make me drowsy.

I owe a letter to Corporal 32413654, Hq and Hq Sq., VII AAF S.C., APO 953, c/o PM San Francisco, Calif., thanking him for the necktie he sent me at Christmas. In 1918 I was a private in the Army. My number was 4,345,016. I was a boy of medium height. I had light hair. I had no absences from duty under G.O. 31, 1912, or G.O. 45, 1914. The number of that war was Number One.

From *The Second Tree from the Corner*

Ogden Nash
[1902-1971]

Ogden Nash was for many years one of America's best-known and widely-loved comic poets. He was born in Rye, New York and attended Harvard University for one year. After a short-lived and unspectacular stint on Wall Street, and an equally brief attempt in advertising, Nash devoted himself successfully to writing. During a career of some forty years, he produced twenty volumes of verse, collaborated on a Broadway musical, and became a popular television panels show personality. Incredible rhymes and outrageous puns were his trademark, putting his unique stamp on every subject imaginable. Whether writing terse, two-line observations or long flowing commentaries in unusual meters, his touch is always precise, light and charming.

THE PIG

The pig, if I am not mistaken,
Supplies us sausage, ham, and bacon.
Let others say his heart is big—
I call it stupid of the pig.

THE COBRA

This creature fills its mouth with venum
And walks upon its duodenum.
He who attempts to tease the cobra
Is soon a sadder he, and sobra.

THE CAMEL

The camel has a single hump;
The dromedary, two;
Or else the other way around.
I'm never sure. Are you?

THE OSTRICH

The ostrich roams the great Sahara.
Its mouth is wide, its neck is narra.
It has such long and lofty legs,
I'm glad it sits to lay its eggs.

THE PORCUPINE

Any hound a porcupine nudges
Can't be blamed for harboring grudges.
I know one hound that laughed all winter
At a porcupine that sat on a splinter.

THE SEA-GULL

Hark to the whimper of the sea-gull;
He weeps because he's not an ea-gull.
Suppose you were, you silly sea-gull,
Could you explain it to your she-gull?

THE LAMA

The one-l lama,
He's a priest.
The two-l llama,
He's a beast.
And I will bet
A silk pajama
There isn't any
Three-l lllama.*

* The author's attention has been called to a type of conflagration known as the three-alarmer. Pooh.

THE COW

The cow is of the bovine ilk;
One end is moo, the other, milk.

THE RHINOCEROS

The rhino is a homely beast,
For human eyes he's not a feast.
Farewell, farewell, you old rhinoceros,
I'll stare at something less prepoceros.

THE PANTHER

The panther is like a leopard,
Except it hasn't been peppered.
Should you behold a panther crouch,
Prepare to say Ouch.
Better yet, if called by a panther,
Don't anther.

THE PORPOISE

I kind of like the playful porpoise,
A healthy mind in a healthy corpus.
He and his cousin, the playful dolphin.
Why they like swimmin like I like golphin.

From *The Bestiary*

IF ANYTHING SHOULD ARISE,
IT ISN'T I

A prepared position Man hankers for
Is parallel to, and above the floor,
For thither retreating horizontally
He evades the issues that charge him frontally.
But pumpkins do not burgeon in Maytime,
And bed is out of bounds in daytime.
A man in pajamas after nine
Transgresses the housewife's Party Line.
He's unethical and unpatriotic,
Unkempt, uncouth, unaristocrotic,
Unwept, unhonored, unsung, unread,
And, if he doesn't get up, unfed.
That is why he smiles when the moment comes
When hands are hot and forehead hums,
When throat is parched and nostrils rankle
And legs are aching from knee to ankle.
Making sure the housewife observes his plight,
He bravely whispers he's quite all right,
What's a spot of fever, a spell of dizziness.
Where's his hat, he is off to business.
So she telephones the office for him,
And stoups of lemonade doth pour him,
And trees his shoes and hangs his clothes up
And introduces drops his nose up,
She fetches toast as light as froth,
And bouillon, consommé and broth,
And be he Harvardite or Yaleite,
She orders him to bed by daylight,
Like Heaven chastening a Baalite
She orders him to bed by daylight.

Beneath the sheets he cracks his knuckles
And chokes to cover up his chuckles,
And coughs a spirited cadenza
In grateful praise of influenza.

Langston Hughes
[1902–1967]

Langston Hughes first created the character of Jesse B. Semple in 1940 for his newspaper columns in the *New York Post* and the *Chicago Defender*. Originally directed mainly toward black readers, these stories about "Simple" and his friends have since been collected in several books, adapted into a musical play, and translated into several languages. Genial, talkative Simple views the problems of life and particularly race relations with down-to-earth and folksy common sense. "To keep from cryin' Ah opens mah mouth an' laughs," Hughes has Simple say.

Hughes was born in Joplin, Missouri, and raised in the Midwest. He wrote his first verse when his grammar school class elected him to write the graduation poem. At the age of nineteen, he attracted national recognition when his famous poem, "The Negro Speaks of Rivers," first appeared in *The Crisis*. He held a variety of jobs in this country, aboard a freighter to Africa, and in Europe before returning to graduate from Lincoln University in Pennsylvania. Regarded worldwide as a distinguished poet, Hughes also produced articles, novels, short fiction, and drama depicting the life of blacks in the United States.

CENSUS

"I have had so many hardships in this life," said Simple, "that it is a wonder I'll live until I die. I was born young, black, voteless, poor, and hungry, in a state where white folks did not even put Negroes on the census. My daddy said he were never counted in his life by the United States government. And nobody could find a birth certificate for me nowhere. It were not until I come to Harlem that one day a census taker dropped around to my house and asked me where were I born and why, also my age and if I was still living. I said, 'Yes, I am here, in spite of all.'

"'All of what?' asked the census taker. 'Give me the data.'

"'All my corns and bunions, for one,' I said. 'I were borned with corns. Most colored peoples get corns so young, they must be inherited. As for bunions, they seem to come natural, we stands on our feet so much. These feet of mine have stood in everything from soup lines to the draft board. They have supported everything from a packing trunk to a hongry woman. My feet have walked ten thousand miles running errands for white folks and another ten thousand trying to keep up with colored. My feet have stood before altars, at crap tables, bars, graves, kitchen doors, welfare windows, and social security railings. Be sure and include my feet on that census you are taking,' I told that man.

"Then I went on to tell him how my feet have helped to keep the American shoe industry going, due to the money I have spent on my feet. 'I have wore out seven hundred pairs of shoes, eighty-nine tennis shoes, forty-four summer sandals, and two hundred and two loafers. The socks my feet have bought could build a knitting mill. The razor blades I have used cutting away my corns could pay for a razor plant. Oh, my feet have helped to make America rich, and I am still standing on them.

" 'I stepped on a rusty nail once, and mighty near had lockjaw. And from my feet up, so many other things have happened to me, since, it is a wonder I made it through this world. In my time, I have been cut, stabbed, run over, hit by a car, tromped by a horse, robbed, fooled, deceived, double-crossed, dealt seconds, and mighty near blackmailed—but I am still here! I have been laid off, fired and not rehired, Jim Crowed, segregated, insulted, eliminated, locked in, locked out, locked up, left holding the bag, and denied relief. I have been caught in the rain, caught in jails, caught short with my rent, and caught with the wrong woman—but I am still here!

" 'My mama should have named me Job instead of Jesse B. Semple. I have been underfed, underpaid, undernourished, and everything but undertaken—yet I am still here. The only thing I am afraid of now—is that I will die before my time. So man, put me on your census now this year, because I may not be here when the next census comes around.'

"The census man said, 'What do you expect to die of—complaining?'

" 'No,' I said, 'I expect to ugly away.' At which I thought the man would laugh. Instead you know he nodded his head, and wrote it down. He were white and did not know I was making a joke. Do you reckon that man really thought I am homely?"

TWO SIDES NOT ENOUGH

"A man ought to have more than just two sides to sleep on," declared Simple. "Now if I get tired of sleeping on my left side, I have nothing to turn over on but my right side."

"You could sleep on your back," I advised.

"I snores on my back."

"Then why not try your stomach?"

"Sleeping on my stomach, I get a stiff neck—I always have to keep my head turned toward one side or the other, else I smothers. I do not like to sleep on my stomach."

"The right side, or the left side, are certainly enough sides for most people to sleep on. I don't know what your trouble is. But, after all, there are two sides to every question."

"That's just what I am talking about," said Simple. "Two sides are not enough. I'm tired of sleeping on either my left side, or on my right side, so I wish I had two or three more sides to change off on. Also, if I sleep on my left side, I am facing my wife, then I have to turn over to see the clock in the morning to find out what time it is. If I sleep on my right side, I am facing the window so the light wakes me up before it is time to get up. If I sleep on my back, I snores, and disturbs my wife. And my stomach is out for sleeping, due to reasons which I mentioned. In the merchant marine, sailors are always talking about the port side and the starboard side of a ship. A human should have not only a left side and a right side, but also a port side and a starboard side."

"That's what left and right mean in nautical terms,"
I said. "You know as well as I do that a ship has only
two sides."

"Then ships are bad off as a human," said Simple.
"All a boat can do when a storm comes up, is like I do
when I sleep—toss from side to side."

"Maybe you eat too heavy a dinner," I said, "or drink
too much coffee."

"No, I am not troubled in no digestion at night,"
said Simple. "But there is one thing that I do not like
in the morning—waking up to face the same old one-
eyed egg Joyce has fried for breakfast. What I wish is
that there was different kinds of eggs, not just white
eggs with a yellow eye. There ought to be blue eggs
with a brown eye, and brown eggs with a blue eye,
also red eggs with green eyes."

"If you ever woke up and saw a red egg with a green
eye on your plate, you would think you had a hangover."

"I would," said Simple. "But eggs *is* monotonous!
No matter which side you turn an egg on, daddy-o, it
is still an egg—hard on one side and soft on the other.
Or, if you turn it over, it's hard on both sides. Once an
egg gets in the frying pan, it has only two sides, too.
And if you burn the bottom side, it comes out just like
the race problem, black and white, black and white."

"I thought you'd get around to race before you got
through. You can't discuss any subject at all without
bringing in color. God help you! And in reducing
everything to two sides, as usual, you oversimplify."

"What does I do?"

"I say your semantics make things too simple."

"My which?"

"Your verbiage."

"My what?"

"Your words, man, your words."

"Oh," said Simple. "Well, anyhow, to get back to
eggs—which is a simple word. For breakfast I wish some
other birds besides chickens laid eggs for eating, with
a different kind of flavor than just a hen flavor. What-

ever you are talking about with your *see-antics*, Jack, at my age a man gets tired of the same kind of eggs each and every day—just like you get tired of the race problem. I would like to have an egg some morning that tastes like a pork chop."

"In that case, why don't you have pork chops for breakfast instead of eggs?"

"Because there is never no pork chops in my icebox in the morning."

"There would be if you would put them there the night before."

"No," said Simple, "I would eat them up the night before—which is always the trouble with the morning after—you have practically nothing left from the night before—except the race problem."

Richard Armour
[1906–   ]

Richard Armour is a distinguished educator as well as a leading American humorist. With a Ph.D. from Harvard, he has been a professor of English, dean and writer-in-residence at several universities, and has served on the faculty of Scripps College for over twenty years. He is the author of scholarly works of biography and criticism as well as a prolific producer of light verse, parody, and satire. Many of his collections of humor reveal the comic underside of academia and present deliciously skewed commentaries on literature and history. Such books as *It All Started with Columbus, Twisted Tales from Shakespeare,* and *The Classics Reclassified* will delight anyone who ever groaned over a textbook.

THE SCARLET LETTER

The story is set in Boston, back in colonial times, when sin was really sinful. Everyone there is a Puritan, since all the other people are either still in England or have gone to Virginia or to hell. The Puritans are a gloomy lot, and by the time the reader gets to the second paragraph, in which the author dwells lovingly on jails and cemeteries, he knows this is no place to be looking for laughs.

As the narrative begins, a crowd has gathered in front of the weather-stained prison door. Growing by the door is a rosebush, and the reader who is alert to such things knows it is a Symbol. Nevertheless, just to be sure, Hawthorne picks one of the roses and explains that this will serve "to symbolize some sweet moral blossom" which, he says, will "relieve the darkening close of a tale of human frailty and sorrow." Hawthorne then presents the rose to the reader, who can either clutch it nervously in his hand while he reads or press it in the book if it is not a library copy.

At last the door of the jail opens, and out comes Hester Prynne, a tall young woman "with a figure of perfect elegance on a large scale." The women among the spectators, all of whom wear petticoats and farthingales and have noses sharp enough to use for letter openers, whisper to each other, hoping Hester can hear. In their humble opinion she is a naughty baggage, a malefactress, and a transgressoress.

What fascinates the onlookers is something embroidered on Hester's bosom or, more accurately, on her dress. It is not only embroidered but illuminated, so that it will be visible by night. This ornament is a SCARLET LETTER. The letter, which the prisoner has fashioned herself with a needle friends smuggled to her in a pincushion, is an "A." Apparently she had intended to go through the alphabet, making a New England sampler, but ran out of thread.

Prodded along by a grim beadle, Hester makes her way to the marketplace, where she climbs up onto the scaffold, without, however, "undergoing that gripe about the neck and confinement of the head, the proneness to which was the most devilish characteristic of this ugly engine." She has an infant in her arms, and what with this and "the heavy weight of a thousand unrelenting eyes," is really burdened down. There she poses with her chin up for hours, while it gradually dawns on the reader that she has sinned and is being punished.

Some time earlier, it seems, Hester was married in England to a gentleman old enough to be her father, or even grandfather, a man with "a pale, thin, scholar-like visage, and eyes dim and bleared by the lamplight." His left shoulder was higher than his right, which was no help either to his looks or to his tailor. What attracted Hester to him Hawthorne does not explain, probably because he was unable to figure it out himself.

Two years before, Hester's husband had sent her to America, saying he would be along later. But he never arrived. Naturally, she assumed he was dead. How was she to know that he had indeed come to America but had fallen into the hands of Indians, who detained him nearly two years, trying to decide whether, with his thinning hair, he was worth scalping?

After a year or so, Hester had grown tired of waiting and had given birth to a child. There was strong suspicion that she had had an accomplice. But who? Everyone was busy guessing. The suspense was mounting, and so was the anxiety of young men about town, improper Bostonians unable to think up an alibi.

Now, standing on the platform, Hester stares back

proudly at the curious Puritans. Suddenly she sees an elderly man whom she recognizes by his "furrowed visage"[1] and by the fact that his left shoulder is a trifle higher than his right. It is her husband! He bends his eyes on her and she fastens hers on him. She clutches her sin-born infant to her heaving bosom until the poor thing is in danger of becoming seasick. Meanwhile her husband's face darkens and "a writhing horror," having "twisted itself across his features," slithers off into the bushes. It gives you the creeps.

Before being returned to prison, Hester is exhorted by the Governor (a political hack who ran on the Puritans First ticket) and other somber dignitaries to confess who is the father of her little bastard. One of the righteous gentlemen who lectures the erring woman is her pastor, the Reverend Arthur Dimmesdale, a nice young clergyman who has large brown melancholy eyes and "a mouth which, unless when he forcibly compressed it, was apt to be tremulous." His mouth is wobbling like jelly when he asks Hester to name her baby's father. Thereupon, lo and behold, her sin-baby lifts up its little arms to the minister so appealingly that one begins to wonder. No, it *couldn't* be!

Back in prison, Hester is visited by her husband, Roger Chillingworth, a cold fish whose name fits him better than his clothes.

Hester is in a state of nervous excitement, and the child, "who, drawing its sustenance from the maternal bosom, seemed to have drunk in with it all the turmoil, the anguish and despair, which pervaded the mother's system," is sick to its little stomach. Chillingworth opens his leathern case and gives Hester and her baby a draught he learned about from the Indians. Hester quaffs it without even glancing at the label, she is that trusting. No wonder the girl is in trouble.

Chillingworth is no M.D., and has had only a basic course in alchemy. Moreover, his bedside manner leaves

---

[1] He was run over by a plow.

much to be desired. Instead of asking Hester how she feels, he asks her who is the father of her child.

"Ask me not!" replies Hester, who is never without an exclamation point. "That thou shalt never know!"

Chillingworth swears he will find her lover. "He bears no letter of infamy wrought into his garment, as thou dost," he hisses, "but I shall read it on his heart." He probably learned how to do this from the Indians, too. Meanwhile Hester must promise not to disclose to anyone that Chillingworth is her husband.

"Breathe not the secret, above all, to the man thou wottest of," says Chillingworth menacingly and then, picking up his leathern case, oozes out. He is up to something, though Hester wots not what.

When her prison term is over, Hester goes to live in a little thatched cottage on the outskirts of town. You'd think she would clear out of there and go to New York or somewhere more congenial to sin. But no, she stubbornly sticks around, for the good of her soul and Hawthorne's plot. She makes her living plying her needle, with which she is so felicitously diligent that she makes no distinction between work and ply.

Always she wears a scarlet letter on her blouse. Research has failed to reveal exactly how she managed it. Did she have one special blouse for show, so to speak, with a scarlet letter on it? Did she have half a dozen blouses, each with its letter? Or did she have one letter, which was detachable and could be switched from blouse to blouse? This is the sort of problem that makes literary scholarship so fascinating.

With Hester lives her child, named Pearl[2] As time passes, she grows into a difficult little girl who is forever asking her mother embarrassing questions about the scarlet letter. As Freud could have told Hester in a minute,[3] her daughter is clearly manifesting a latent

---

[2] Perhaps because she is slightly unstrung.

[3] Though, to justify his fee, he would have taken considerably longer.

consciousness of sex. Townspeople think Hester a bad influence, and the Governor, who seems to have no more important state business, is about to take Pearl from her mother when the Reverend Mr. Dimmesdale intervenes, his mouth wobbling like mad. Henceforth he clutches his heart each time he speaks, and one need not be a cardiologist to know that the old ticker cannot stand this sort of mauling for long.

Meanwhile Roger Chillingworth, the wronged husband, remains in town, setting himself up as a physician without a license. His professional services are welcomed, because the only other surgeon is the local barber, who can start a flow of blood but has difficulty stopping it. Chillingworth's favorite patient is the sickening Mr. Dimmesdale,[4] who is getting paler and thinner every day, in part because of his practice of fasting "to keep the grossness of his earthly state from clogging and obscuring his spiritual lamp."[5] Since he continues to decline, "Doc" Chillingworth applies leeches to his veins, where they slurp away merrily. Poor Mr. Dimmesdale fails to become more robust, but the leeches grow so fat they can hardly waddle off to the next patient.

Chillingworth now moves in with the young preacher, not merely to save house calls but to make it possible for him "to go deep into his patient's bosom, delving among his principles, prying into his recollections, and probing everything with a cautious touch, like a treasure-seeker in a dark cavern." Sigmund Chillingworth may have no medical degree, but all that time he claims to have spent with the Indians he was probably in Vienna.

In short, Chillingworth is beginning to think Mr. Dimmesdale is his man. One day, coming on the preacher while he is napping, he unbuttons the fellow's

[4] There are some who think Dimmesdale absolutely nauseating.
[5] What he needs is a new wick.

vestments and takes a look at his chest. Hawthorne does not tell us what he saw that caused such a wild expression of wonder, horror, and joy. Mayhap his patient's id, for which he had been groping these many weeks, had surfaced for air. At any rate, he is convinced that (1) the Reverend Mr. Dimmesdale is Pearl's father and (2) perseverance pays.

Now, without letting him know he knows, Chillingworth gives his patient the full treatment. This includes feeding his vitamin-rich weeds he picks from the tops of graves. Mr. Dimmesdale, responding encouragingly, gets worse and worse. He takes to looking at himself in the mirror under a green light. He also lashes himself across the shoulders with a bloody scourge he keeps in his bloody scourge closet. When the weather is thoroughly foul, he goes for a walk all unbuttoned.

One particularly ugly night Mr. Dimmesdale goes walking in strange company. He is pushed along by Remorse and pulled back by her sister, Cowardice, probably a couple of tipsy parishioners. Suddenly he finds himself at the foot of the scaffold on which Hester earlier had displayed her red badge, discouraged. Mounting it, he vows to confess his sin at last, knowing full well that it is too dark for anybody to see him and that the townspeople have been in bed since 9 P.M.

Beastly night as it is, Hester and Pearl just happen by, and Mr. Dimmesdale invites them up onto the platform. There they join hands in a circle and make a pretty family picture, a fine example of Togetherness.

"Wilt thou stand here with Mother and me, to-morrow noontide?" inquires Pearl with her usual knack for asking embarrassing questions.

"Nay, not so, my little Pearl," replies the minister, who is inclined to procrastinate. He suggests a somewhat later date, such as Judgment Day.

About this time there is a meteor flash, and M. Dimmesdale thinks he sees a great scarlet A in the sky.[6]

---

[6] It was a red-letter night.

He may only be imagining things. However, he actually does see Roger Chillingworth, who all the while has been lurking in the bushes with pad and pencil. Chillingworth, a combination roving reporter and house detective, is always on hand when anything interesting happens. He was even in the closet when Mr. Dimmesdale was whipping himself, hiding behind a pile of surplus surplices.

But Mr. Dimmesdale's secret shame is still not revealed to the public. Chillingworth, who fancies himself a sort of colonial Marquis de Sade, wants to torture the sinner for a while. Thus seven years pass, with no more than the turn of a page. Hester is becoming tolerated locally. People have got so they even say "Howdy, thou" to her, but she puts her finger to her lips and points to her bosom. Far from being ashamed, she seems proud.[7]

While Hester has been getting almost unbearably saintly, Chillingworth has turned into a devil. "There came a glare of red light out of his eyes," Hawthorne says. Hester goes to him and begs him to stop persecuting Mr. Dimmesdale. Look what it is doing to his own bloodshot eyes. But Chillingworth laughs ("Ha! ha!") in her face. He is enjoying himself. However, Mr. Dimmesdale has run out of laughs, now even scourging himself listlessly.

All this time Hester, who is better than most women about keeping a secret, has not told Mr. Dimmesdale that Roger Chillingworth is her wronged husband. But one day, meeting the minister in the woods, she tells him, and he is taken aback aplenty. His physician! His roommate! Come to think of it, the fellow *has* been acting a little odd, chuckling in that pleased way every time his patient has a heart attack.

After seven lean years, Mr. Dimmesdale decides he has had it. A ship for England is in harbor, and he and

---

[7] Of which, the letter or her bosom, Hawthorne does not make clear.

Hester and Pearl will flee to the Old World and start life anew. He begins to pack his vestments, and Hester fills a suitcase with needles.

It looks as if they are to escape. While Hester is happily planning to toss the Scarlet Letter into the ocean, Mr. Dimmesdale, in a burst of enthusiasm and fellowship, has the impulse to tell one of his parishioners a dirty joke. Unfortunately the impulse passes before he can think of one.

Now, alas, Hester learns from the shipmaster that he has booked another passenger for the voyage, one Chillingworth, Roger! This, we must agree, is a tough break. Of course they might drop Roger over the side in mid-ocean, along with the Scarlet Letter, but such a sensible solution does not come to mind. They can think only of dinner at the captain's table, or their morning constitutional around the deck, or a game of quoits or shuffleboard—with Chillingworth's demonic cackle in their ears and his bright red eyes peering from behind a life raft.

Fortunately, there is one way to get out of this apparent impasse, and Hawthorne takes it. As Mr. Dimmesdale strolls through the marketplace, receiving the congratulations of the townspeople on one of his most hypocritical sermons, he sees Hester and Pearl standing by the very scaffold on which they had stood in shame a couple of hundred pages back. Seized by an impulse,[8] he mounts the platform, signaling them to join him. And who climbs up there with them, uninvited as usual? None other than Chillingworth, Roger!

The Reverend Mr. Dimmesdale now confesses. To wit, he sinned just one little sin, and look at all the trouble he caused. Thereupon he drops dead, but not before tearing open his shirt to bare his chest, on which some of the spectators later testify to having seen a SCARLET LETTER, exactly like Hester's! As to how it got

[8] Hawthorne's—to end the novel.

there, opinions vary. A plausible theory is that it was caused by "the ever-active tooth of remorse, gnawing from the inmost heart outwardly," a little like a gopher. Then again it may only have been a rash.

After Mr. Dimmesdale's confession and demise, Chillingworth, having lost his only patient, gives up his medical practice. Gradually he shrivels up and, within the year, expires, or blows away. Hester disappears from the colony for a while, but eventually comes back and spends the rest of her life Doing Good. She continues to wear the scarlet letter on her bosom, but now instead of a stigma it has become a tourist attraction.

When Hester dies, she is buried in the graveyard, where a single tombstone suffices for her and for Mr. Dimmesdale. With admirable succinctness, the only engraving on it is the letter A. We would fain commend such New England thrift.

Questions on "The Scarlet Letter"

1. If you saw a young woman today with an "A" on her bosom, would you think she was:
    a. Absolutely top grade?
    b. Going steady with an Amherst boy?
2. Conscientious though he was about his pastoral duties, did the Reverend Mr. Dimmesdale have to do *everything* himself? Didn't he have an assistant?
3. Hester is said to have made her living with her needle. Did she give inoculations on the side? If not on the side, in the arm?
4. Has it ever occurred to you that Pearl might have come out of an oyster?
5. What could Chillingworth have seen on Mr. Dimmesdale's chest that was so startling:
    a. An unusual amount of hair?
    b. Notes for a sermon?
6. Take two symbols and clash them together. Did you forget to keep your fingers in your ears?

7. What if Hester and her preacher friend had gotten away from Chillingworth and gone back to England? Could they ever have been truly happy, accompanied by Shame, Remorse, and Pearl?

8. For collateral reading, look up the stories of Hester, Rose, and Daisy in Van Wyck Brooks' *The Flowering of New England.*

Sam Levenson
[1911–   ]

Sam Levenson's twentieth-century wit shares the homespun spirit of an earlier America. His frontier was East Harlem, with its wagon trains of pushcarts and homesteads of tenement houses. After fifteen years as a high school Spanish teacher and guidance counselor, Levenson emerged as a comic performer before educational, civic, and religious groups. Today he is a popular television personality and the author of several best-selling books, including *Everything but Money*. Levenson's warm humor draws on his deep sense of family, his ethnic origins, and strong human values. "The home is the cosmos," he has said, "with Mama and Papa the moon and the sun, and the children the planets."

FROM
EVERYTHING BUT MONEY

In those days people did not live as long as they do today, but things lived longer. In our house old things were not discarded but retired to a drawer in the kitchen which we called "Mama's shame-to-throw-out drawer." Every family had one. It contained at all times such indispensables as half a pair of scissors, a toothless comb, eyeglass frames without lenses, empty Vaseline jars, a knotted rubber band, the face of a clock, a black button marked "Off," the bulb of a nasal spray, a fountain-pen tube, a ball of tinfoil, a key to the old apartment, and a "gold" medal which read "Best Wishes Thom McAn Shoes."

The drawer was appropriately lined with old newspaper, of which there was always a great abundance, since news, too, did not have to be new to be good. Mama saw no reason for buying new news when she had not yet used up the old.

Newspapers, in fact, served many functions besides covering the news; they also covered the floors, for instance. After the lady of the house had washed her wooden floors she covered them with newspaper, wall to wall. Many a time I came home from school to find Mama stretched out on the floor absorbed in an editorial.

The rotogravure section was reserved for sideboard-drawer lining because its brownish-red color matched our genuine imitation mahogany. The bottom drawer was known as the Maternity Ward. When our cat was expecting (again), Mama shredded a newspaper with

135

her meat chopper and padded the drawer. Women understood such things. At our house kittens could read before they could walk.

I inherited most of my hats from older brothers, uncles, and forgetful strangers, who got them that way themselves. The size was reduced to fit my head by folding a string of newspaper under the inside leather band.

Party hats were fashioned of cleverly folded newspaper, as were generals' hats, Chinese hats, chefs' hats, kings' crowns, sailboats, bandits' masks, megaphones, telescopes, and fly swatters.

A short, hand-rolled wad of newspaper served as a cork for bottles as well as a packing for keyholes when privacy was desired. (Keyholes were for looking, not for locking.)

We cut our schoolbook covers out of newspaper. My brother Mike could work it out so that an inspiring picture of Tom Mix's horse would appear smack on the front of the book.

Children were punished by being slapped on the head with a rolled-up newspaper. I must say, though, that no father was cruel enough to swat a kid with the Sunday paper. This might leave him punchy through the following Thursday.

Mama and my sister Dora cut newspapers into dress patterns—for fancy dresses the society page, for daily wear the Situations Wanted.

If any parts of the newspaper survived they were stored in the cellar for months. Eventually they were sold to the junk dealer who then sold the lot to the newspaper publisher whose mother probably had lots of floors to cover.

While we did not possess the purchasing power to buy first-class merchandise, we did possess the willpower to be first-class human beings. Things could become junk, but people didn't have to accept such a fate. Man could fight back. A teapot, Mama said, had no soul, but man did.

Mama had a philosopher's insight and a prophet's foresight. She foresaw the corrupting effect of vermin not only on beds but on people in the beds, the gnawing of rats not only on plaster but on the moral fiber of humans. Dirt is bad company. Dirty beds could breed dirty thoughts which could breed dirty deeds.

Mama, therefore, practiced preventive housekeeping. Capitulation to a second-class physical environment might mean the renunciation of first-class ideals. Personal honor, behavior, and character could never be "marked down." Mama's search for defects in the quality of our values was far more exacting than her appraisal of a pushcart bargain. She made it pretty clear that our home was not a pushcart, and that our integrity would not be reduced. Mama insisted that we were a first-class family, and that among the few treasures she could afford in life was a clean home.

Her fight against dirt was based upon the premise that circumstance makes poor, but people make dirt, and that if everyone cleaned his own house inside and out, the whole world would be clean. If Mama had to contend with the environment, the environment would have to contend with Mama. She was the environment's problem.

Some housekeepers threw in the mop: "You want dirt? I'll show you dirt!" Mama reacted with spite. "You want dirt? Not from me. I'll show you who's boss in this house! I'll show you clean like you never saw clean. I'll kill you with cleanliness." She did, in fact, almost kill my brother Albert, who ran through a closed window onto the fire escape to watch a parade going by. Mrs. Clean had polished the window to the point where it was invisible. The day Mrs. Gordon, upstairs, forgot to clean her windows Mama was quick to remark, "Next thing you know she'll start using lipstick."

Today psychiatrists would call Mama a compulsive

housekeeper. She would get up at 6 A.M. mumbling, "Here it is Monday, before you know it Tuesday, and Wednesday just around the corner, and Thursday running into Friday, and I haven't done a stitch of work yet."

Bedmaking in our house began earlier than in most, and more suddenly. It started with either three or four of us on the bedroom floor, depending on which bed Mama overturned first. If we didn't come to quickly enough we often found ourselves folded up in a mattress on the fire escape. Or Mama would pretend to be considerate. She wouldn't wake you. "You want to sleep? Sleep. Sleep. Sleep." And she would pull the sheet out from under you, start pounding the pillows with a carpet beater, and proceed to make the bed with you in it.

One morning I was sent home by my teacher: "Young man, you look sick. Go right home and tell your mother to put you to bed." I walked into the house to find Mama in her customary position—on her knees, wet rag in hand, next to a pail of sudsy-gray water. "The teacher said I'm sick and that I should lie down in bed."

Mama looked up. "In what? Are you sure you can't sit up? I just made the bed!"

Mama would sooner have been caught drunk than have anyone, especially a stranger, walk in and find her house dirty. My brothers used to joke about it: "Mama's ashamed to leave dirty dishes in the sink overnight. If a burglar broke in she would be embarrassed."

At our house "The line is busy" meant that Mama was hanging out the wash. On Monday at dawn you were wakened by the twittering of hysterical sparrows trying to reply to the squealing of the clothesline pulleys. By noon all the women had hung their laundry. All light was shut out of the yard by the hundreds of garments crisscrossing each other to form an impenetrable forest of wet wash.

In that yard I picked up a working knowledge of sex.

By studying the wash, I could determine whether Mrs. Burns' daughters were now "big girls" by the appearance of brassieres and panties, or whether they were still "little girls" who wore woolen bloomers.

My mother had an all-male line of "union suits" (closed shop but for the trap door), with the exception of her own long nightgowns which hung down two full flights when they were wet, and my sister Dora's skirts which dripped in Technicolor onto other people's white laundry.

My job on Mondays was to "run down into the yard and pick up the handkerchiefs that fell off the line before someone takes them." The reason I didn't like to go was that some window would invariably fly open and an angry woman would call down to me, "What are you doing there?"

"I'm picking up my mother's handkerchiefs."

"They're mine, not your mother's." Other windows would open. The battle was on.

"They're not his and they're not yours. They're mine."

"And how do you know they're yours?"

"If I don't know mine who knows mine?"

"And I know mine."

"May I not live to see my daughter married if it's not mine."

"Don't swear for a handkerchief. It doesn't pay. It's not a tablecloth."

It would take days before peace was restored.

The difference between keeping things clean and keeping kids clean was that things just sat still and waited for the dirt to collect. We kids were carriers. We ran a pickup and delivery service.

If you brought dirt into the house your name was mud. A kangaroo court was in session at all times. Mama would line up the eight kids against the kitchen wall, one hand pointing at us accusingly, the other pointing up to the evidence: the mark of a rubber ball on the ceiling. What she said does not seem to make much sense now, but it did then. "I just scrubbed that ceiling on my hands and knees and now look. Who did it?"

Sometimes when we walked into the house we would get a wet rag square in the face for two reasons: one, to clean; two, to identify. "Let me see which slob it is." Mama sometimes cleaned off the grimy little faces of total strangers. "You I don't know. Out!"

If Mama didn't happen to have a rag in her hand she wiped your face with the edge of her apron which she had moistened with *your* spit. "Here, spit on this." Obviously she knew it was unsanitary for us to use other people's spit.

It wasn't that we kids loved dirt; we simply valued time more. Keeping clean used up too much of a kid's valuable minutes. There was so much to do. There was ink to be spilled, chalk to be stepped on, toothpaste to be squirted, pencil shavings to be scattered, and windows to be fingerprinted.

It's hard to believe that dirt could overcome hunger, but it did.

"Ma, I'm hungry."

"Wash your hands; I'll give you a piece of bread and butter."

"I'm not hungry."

One of Mama's favorite teaching techniques was comparison—impossible us versus some paragon of elegance. "Does President Coolidge hang his dirty socks on a doorknob? Answer me! Does Rudolph Valentino leave his sneakers on his bed? Answer me! Does Chaim Weizmann chew his tie? Does the Prince of Wales throw newspaper into his mother's toilet bowl?"

When all else failed Mama made the announcement that put fear in our hearts. "All right; enough is enough. Tomorrow the Board of Health is coming to take you all away. Good-bye."

Came Monday morning however, you wouldn't have recognized us. We had to be thoroughly clean, even where it didn't show, like inside the ears "you shouldn't give me any excuses that you didn't hear what the teacher said." Our hands had to be scrubbed clean as a surgeon's notwithstanding brother Albert's claim that "I never raise my hand in class, anyhow." In school it was essential not only to spell good, but to smell good. You even had to put on a fresh, clean shirt. On lesser occasions, if you got caught putting on a clean shirt Mama would say, "Take it off before you get it dirty."

For school we had to take a bath. "Scratching, like borrowing, helps only for a while," Mama said. We reluctantly turned in our bodies to Mama and submitted to Operation Skin Removal. We resisted, connived, lied, and finally ran out of effective evasions. "It's not dirt; it's my tan from last summer" had been used too often, as had "It's too soon after my cold." We made token attempts at cleanliness by following the spray truck on the street, rubbing our faces and arms in the muddy mist it left in its wake. We walked in the rain face up. Before putting on a fresh shirt we determined whether it had long sleeves or short, and washed ourselves accordingly.

Any one of us who of his own free will just went and took a bath (like brother David who was unnaturally neat for a child) had a lot of explaining to do. "What's the matter you're taking a bath, you going to the doctor or something?"

We knew about cleanliness being next to Godliness, but taking a bath in our home was next to impossible. For six days a week our bathtub served as a storage bin for paint cans, brushes, wine jugs, umbrellas, toilet plungers, soiled laundry, and a day-to-day supply of coal. Before we could be bathed, the tub had to be scoured and the bathroom sealed off. There was a broken window over the bathtub, which had never been replaced. We covered it with a board that the boys referred to as the "draft board." Since there was never a supply of water hot enough to deterge urgent cases like ours, steaming reinforcements were brought to the scene in teakettles, pots and pans. After Mama had made the elbow test (if the skin blistered it was just right), we were thrown in en masse to soak, like laundry. Since the stopper was always missing, we seated a soft, fat brother at the drain end.

Mama washed kids like she washed floors. She tore through our scalps with a horse brush soaked in naphtha sap. We screamed in pain as the acids ate into every aperture. To kill the lice she added kerosene. "Please, Ma! Enough!" Not yet. Her fingers dug into both your ears, twisting, turning, brainwashing mercilessly. You were left draped over the rim of the tub in a state of amnesia, recognizing nobody, frothing at the mouth, promising to be a good boy in the future, ready to sign any confession.

This fierce bathing ritual was another expression of Mama's constant battle against the environment. As I lay in my clean bed recovering from the ordeal by water I knew the great joy of pride in one's body. My self-esteem had been lifted. I felt important, fresh, redeemed. I was glad to be alive and very much in love with the world and my home. The sin of dirt which the street had inflicted upon me had been washed away, and I was reborn, a first-class citizen, the equal of any kid.

Years later, the older boys, who were beginning to earn money, hired a woman to come once a week to help Mama. On the day she was due, Mama got up at five-thirty, scrubbed the floors, and put up fresh curtains: "Nobody should think we're pigs." When the lady arrived, Mama had hot coffee ready for her. They compared aches and pains, including a few heartaches, recipes, husbands, children, and blood pressures. When she left they cried on each other's shoulders, and Mama promised to come and help her with her house real soon.

When Papa married Mama he put a ring on one of her fingers and thimbles on all the others. Without benefit of bifocals she could thread a needle in the dark with one hand, tie a knot with her teeth, and chop meat with her free hand. She pumped away at her sewing machine like a six-day bicycle rider, used up enough energy to go around the world three times, and never left home.

Long pants were belittled into short pants; old skirts became new aprons; old aprons became good as new collars; collars were reversed and re-reversed; sleeves were amputated to the elbow; cuffs were successfully transplanted and grafted onto strange pants— and the scar never showed. All garments, outer or under, public or private, mentionable or unmentionable, could be made to fit anyone. "Use it up, wear it out; make it do or do without." If your sleeves were short you got longer mittens. Padding the size of beanbags took care of sloping shoulders, and flour sacks expanded the crotches of narrow-minded undershorts. Besides, whatever Mama Levenson couldn't fill in, Father Time would: "He'll grow into it." Mama was not concerned with fashion but with nakedness. "It's good enough for us now." We were never sure how long now would be.

Clothing was always en route from one kid to another. Typical conversations ran something like this:

"Ma, where's my shirt?"

"Which shirt?"

"The one that used to be Albert's jumper that used to be Jack's sport shirt that used to be Dora's blouse."

"Oh, that one? Too late. It's Albert's underwear now."

Mama hated holes the way nature abhors a vacuum. A rip was followed immediately by a patch. The colors of her patches were brilliant, and no two were alike. When brother Bill bent over, he looked like a stained-glass window.

Mama cut up the oldest blankets to patch the older ones. The old blankets were not even used. They were considered too new to be put on the beds.

Even a hole in the head was covered with a patch,

not necessarily white, and certainly not sterile, but effective. The germs died of overpopulation.

The knot was a handy device for tying off poverty. If one of us kids tore his shoelace, he didn't pull out the remainder and discard it. It was cheaper to make a knot and lace the shoe only three-quarters of the way up. After the next break came more knots. The lace usually ended up outlasting the shoe.

If the top button of your shorts tore off you could pull the section where the button had been through the buttonhole, then tie a knot into it, and it would hold better than a button.

Between the hours of after supper and bedtime Mama could always be found knitting things for the family: "Here, hold out your hands." I would hold taut a skein of wool while she rolled it into a ball. She was off on a new project. Often there were mystery knittings. "A surprise for you; something you need." This was no help at all because I needed everything. It never fit the one for whom it was intended, but there were so many of us that it was bound to fit at least one.

The whole family watched in fascination as the thing began to take form. When I saw it had no fingers, I decided it was a mitten. When she left off the thumb, I decided it was a hat. When she left off the woolly knob on top, I decided it was socks after all, especially because she had measured my hand. Mama operated on the well-known scientific fact that the circumference of the fist is equal to the length of the foot. The socks Mama knitted had a heavy inner seam. It felt like walking barefoot on the blade of an ice skate. If we complained she would say, "They don't appreciate anything."

Our flat was lit by gaslight. It always happened that when we had company the gas flame would begin to sputter and fade, a deliberate attempt on the part of the public utilities to embarrass us. We would hold a tribal council. Brother Joe would be hoisted up to examine the delicate gauze mantle. The slightest twitch of the hand, and it would crumble into a fine gray ash, and the slightest twitch did not fail to materialize. The problem was now half solved. We could prove we had a broken mantle on our hands.

We now had to face the possibility that we were also out of gas. We never accepted this alternative until we had tried to massage the heart of the gas meter. It trembled a bit, but still no heartbeat. The meter had lots of clocks and indicators and numbers. We rotated the knobs like safecrackers, fingered the dials, tried mouth-to-mouth resuscitation by blowing into the coin slot, poked toothpicks into every opening. We tried every known method of revivification short of depositing a quarter, hoping for the miracle of the tenement—light without money.

Now that enough time has elapsed for our family to be immune from prosecution I can confess that sometimes these tricks worked. We could prolong the life of a meter by two or three days. We don't know how it happened, but on one occasion my brother Bill, who had developed strong fingers from tuning his ukulele, forced a dial to the point where we not only had free gas for a month, but got a refund from the company.

Electricity didn't come into our house until we were all grown up. Even then we were restricted to only essential use of the electric lights. If you threw the switch for some silly reason such as to see where you were going, Papa would appear out of the shadow with a "Hello, Mr. Rockefeller." A light on all night meant somebody was in trouble. "Let him have the bulb; he's sick." Under the best of conditions no bulb was ever more than twenty-five watts. Public Futilities, Jack called them.

In many ways our flat anticipated the "Automatic Home of Tomorrow" one reads about in the magazines. We had a "deep-freeze" unit directly outside the kitchen window—with real snow on it. It defrosted itself automatically each spring.

The kitchen sink had "swing-easy" faucets which swung round and round and finally came off in your hand. Nearly all faucets were optimistically marked "Hot." We could tell the difference by watching them drip: the "Cold" dripped warm and the "Hot" dripped rusty. On winter days the cold wind came up through the Hot faucet.

There was "indirect lighting" from the street lamp outside. The problem of kitchen odors was solved by "exhaust ventilation" via a "recessed" hole in the ceiling that heated the "sunken living room" of the apartment upstairs.

Cabinet doors were operated by "remote control." If you banged the front door the dish closet in the kitchen ejected a shelf of ready-cracked dishes. We had automatic dishwashers, too. In those days they were called children.

Our kitchen table would today be called "functional" or "multipurpose." On the same table where the brothers did homework, Mama rolled dough (many a missing report card turned up in a spongecake), Dora ironed laundry, Jack cut up frogs, and Mike practiced handstands. Man! That's togetherness! (It was Mike's handstands that ultimately created a "drop leaf" at the end of the table.)

By placing an ironing board across two chairs you could seat and feed four dinner guests. If the company stayed over, the very same "miracle table" could be expanded by inserting enough boards to sleep four people comfortably.

In addition to rooms each of which was approximately the size and shape of a closet, we had a "walk-in closet" next to the door to our apartment. The boys called it the "good-night closet." Departing guests used to say politely "Good night" and politely walk into the closet.

When one of the boys showed Mama her first magazine picture of a real modern streamlined kitchen she said, "God forbid. It looks like a hospital."

Several pieces of furniture stand out in my memory. There was an item common to the era known as the "lounge," a cross between a bed of nails, an examination table, and a psychiatrist's couch. In the summer it sweated by itself. If you took a nap on it in mid-afternoon you had to be peeled off like a Band-Aid.

Our bureau had knobs all over. Most of them were purely decorative, but the real ones were easy to detect; they came out when you pulled them. It had three drawers. The handles for the top drawer had been removed and placed in the bottom drawer so they wouldn't get lost. You couldn't get at the bottom drawer, except through the middle drawer. The handles for the middle drawer were in the top drawer. The top drawer could only be opened with a crowbar, which is why we called it the "breakfront." Once you had the top drawer out, you put in your hands and forced out the middle drawer, then stuck your hands into where the middle drawer had been and forced out the bottom drawer where you found the knobs to the top drawer. If one of us asked Papa for a penny he would say, "Look in the middle drawer." That would keep us busy for an afternoon.

There was also a china closet, which originally had sharp edges that Papa had rounded off in the process of scratching his back against them. This china closet contained the "good dishes" which were used only if "people" came. The immediate family was not "people." When we moved, the "good dishes" were placed on top of the barrels for "people" to see.

Every family had a wooden icebox in the kitchen. Many of these were quite handsome, with elaborate carving; some were even topped with a mirror.

According to the geologists the ice age ended thousands of years ago—except in our home, where Mama kept it alive for years. It ended officially only after we threw out our icebox. My mother could keep a piece of ice going for weeks. She managed this by various methods.

1. Unless an emergency develops, don't open the icebox. Opening causes melting, and melting is not healthy for ice. (To this day, when I open the refrigerator door I expect to hear a voice say, "Close the icebox.")
2. Never put food into the icebox. Food will also melt the ice. The best place for food is outside the window.

There were several ways of transporting ice from the ice docks to our house.

1. *The old baby carriage.* You placed the ice where the baby would normally sit and covered it with a warm blanket to protect it from the sun's rays and life's hard knocks.
2. *The homemade wagon.* This was an old fruit box nailed onto a shaft, which traveled either on a pair of broken-down roller skates or a set of wobbly spoke-impoverished wheels.
3. *The rope method.* You tied a piece of rope around the cake of ice and dragged same over the sidewalks. We were expert at the art of gently sliding the ice from the sidewalk into the gutter and up again without cracking it. Sometimes pieces did break off in spite of our best efforts. We brought the detached chunks home in our pockets or carried them under our armpits until it became too painful. Little chips were ours to enjoy. You put them into your mouth and sucked them. If you managed to get the ice home safely, all you got was a scolding for bringing such a small piece. "Send an infant for something . . ."

"It is not good for man to be alone," Papa used to say, quoting from the *Poor Man's Almanac of Rationalizations*—so we slept in various sets: four in a bed (the group plan); three in a bed (semiprivate, unless

one of the three had a contagious disease, in which
case he was allowed to sleep with only one, preferably
one who had never had the disease); two in a bed
(doubleheader); and one in a bed (critical list).
Hopeless cases slept in Mama's bed. Chairs and floors
also served as beds. Floors were preferred because you
could not fall off.

In order to insure a reasonable amount of air not
already filtered through our bed partner's adenoids, we
slept not tête-à-tête but foot-à-tête—cross-ventilation we
called it—an arrangement that made it impossible to
cough into a brother's face; we could cough only into
his feet.

There were other sleeping patterns such as crisscross,
tick-tack-toe, checkerboard, pyramids and shambles. A
sudden sneeze by the kid in the middle of any of these
configurations could trigger a chain reaction which sent
kids flying in all directions.

The procedure of getting bedded down for the night
often started with the shock treatment. Just before
bedtime Mama would reel in the clothesline, remove
several sheets of ice which earlier in the day had been
sheets of linen, put them on your bed and say, "Go to
bed." Those were the nights when nobody fought to
be first in bed. Mama would reduce the intensity of
the shock by placing a hot stove lid wrapped in a towel
at your feet. I still carry the name of the stove manu-
facturer branded on my left arch.

Some people brag that they sleep like a rock. I slept
on one. Mama's pillows were about the size of a home
movie screen and were as hard as bags of cement. You
slept with your head propped up as though you were
lying in state. Years later, as we got married, Mama
made each of us a present of a set of pillows extracted
from the mother pillow. Still, no matter how much
stuffing Mama pulled out of the original, it never got
softer.

For most people, sound sleep implies quiet. We
slept through the sounds of a world that never slept.

Our nervous systems were geared to noise. Silence would have shocked us. We slept through the din of fire engines, trolleys, trucks, trains, slamming doors, barking dogs and wailing cats. Within our own walls plumbing hummed, faucets chirped, bedsprings twanged, stoves hissed, mattresses groaned, floors creaked, windows banged, and the window shades wildly applauded all the performances.

While there was room for all to sleep, quilts were at a premium, as were brothers with warm feet. The latter sold high on the open market. Deals for quilts were made before bedtime. We called it the Cover Charge. "Hey, Al! If you let me have the heavy quilt tonight I'll give you my searchlight for lend for two days." The heavy quilt was not warm, just heavy, but therein lay its merit. It didn't slide off the bed. It rested there like a mound of earth on a fresh grave, and we slept the sleep of the just. That quilt could cover three of us, if one of us were not my brother Mike, who was not just a restless sleeper—he was a night crawler. He would start moving across the bed on a forty-five-degree angle from the footboard to the headboard, instinctively dragging the quilt along his route. We held on for dear life and he dragged us, quilt and all, wherever he was going. The tug-of-war lasted until we all fell asleep from sheer exhaustion.

Papa's heavy coat was a prize. He had brought it from the old, cold country and it was lined with fur. We would slip our feet through the sleeves, button ourselves into the hairy straitjacket, and hibernate for one winter's night at a time.

The coldest room in the house was the front room. To get any warmth into it you would have had to open the windows. Mama used to keep her marinated fish there. In order to survive the night in that room you wore a sweater under your undershirt, and long woolen socks. But Mother Nature, not nearly so kind as our own mother, had a way of taunting us on extra-cold nights. Just when you were nice and warm, the call came. You tried to throw her off your track by concentrating on deserts, droughts, sand dunes, or petrified forests—all to no avail.

"Hey, Al. Come with me. It's dark." It was not the dark alone I was afraid of. There was the ghoulish red face of the hot coal stove and, even more frightening, the phosphorescent glow of Mama's teeth in a glass in the kitchen.

Al wouldn't come. "Not me, buddy."

"I'll give you my searchlight for lend for *three* days."

"Make it a week."

"O.K. If you throw in the heavy quilt."

"It's a deal."

Together we made the trip to the toilet dragging the bartered quilt after us lest some older brother roll up in it and claim seniority rights.

Talking about toilets may not be in the best of taste, but neither was living in a tenement with a toilet in the yard. (Brother David referred back to it years later as our Cabaña Club.) The words "Ma, throw me down the key" or "Ma, we're out of orange wrappers" have a very special connotation to the alumni of the tenements.

A night call might require a hike down five flights of stairs in your underwear, struggling all the while to retain your dignity, your sleep, and whatever it was you were retaining. Some tenement dwellers kept a chamber pot under their beds, usually part of a set referred to by tenement wits as a "baseball set—a pitcher on the bureau and a catcher under the bed." Rich people also owned these sets, but theirs were porcelain. In our building the chamber was usually a zinc pail which, when used on a crisp, cold night, could create the effect of a whining fire-engine siren. Wise guys used to open the window and yell, "Where's the fire?"

Max Shulman
[1919–   ]

In a writing career devoted to humor, Max Shulman has produced best-selling novels, long-running plays, successful motion picture scripts, a popular television series, and hundreds of hilarious magazine stories. Born in St. Paul, he was educated at the University of Minnesota, where he edited the campus humor magazine. Shulman continued to lampoon college life in his later writings, such as *Affairs of Dobie Gillis,* from which the following selection is taken. He has also skillfully satirized military service, civilians, government bureaucracy, class values, and virtually every other aspect of contemporary America.

THE UNLUCKY WINNER

My next girl is going to be honest. I don't care if she looks like a doorknob. Just so she's honest.

This determination arises from a late unhappy attachment to one Clothilde Ellingboe. Now, don't misunderstand; I'm not calling Clothilde a crook. Let's say she was irresponsible. Or unethical. Or unprincipled. Or amoral. Let's not go around calling ladies crooks. Watch that stuff.

I met Clothilde at the University of Minnesota's annual Freshman Prom. I was standing in the stag line and I saw her dancing with a fellow halfway across the floor. They were doing the "Airborne Samba," the latest dance craze at the university. In the "Airborne Samba" the girl locks her hands behind the fellow's neck and he carries her all through the dance. She never touches the floor; she just lashes out rhythmically with her feet.

I cut in on them, laughing lightly at the resultant abrasions. I transported Clothilde through the rest of the medley, and then we went out on the terrace for some air. There, in a very short time, I knew I was hers. How vivacious she was! How socially aware she was! You would never believe she was only a freshman, the way she had been everywhere and had done everything and knew everyone. In a very short time I was, as I say, hers.

Then began a social whirl that I would not have thought possible. We were out every night—dancing, movies, sleigh rides, hayrides, wiener roasts, bridge games, community sings. Not a night did we miss.

153

At first I was a little worried. "Clothilde," I would say, "I'd love to go out tonight, but I've got homework. I've got to translate ten pages of Virgil for Latin tomorrow."

"Dobie, you oaf," she would laugh. "Don't you know *anything?*"

Then she would produce a Virgil pony—a Latin textbook with English translations set in smaller type beneath each line of Latin.

When I said that I had to do some work in political science, she would hand me a syllabus that condensed the whole course into an hour's easy reading. If I was concerned about an English history quiz, she would come up with a card the size of a bookmark on which there was printed the dates of all the kings in the British dynasty, plus thumbnails of all significant events.

"This is all very well," I said one night, "but I don't feel that I'm learning anything."

"To the contrary, Dobie," she replied, taking my hands in hers. "Without all this social life, you could never become a well-rounded-out personality. What's more important, Dobie—to know a lot of old facts and figures or to become a well-rounded-out personality?"

"To become a well-rounded-out personality," I said. "Clearly."

"There you are," she said, spreading her palms. "C'mon, Dobie, let's go down to the Kozy Kampus Kave and hear E-String Eddie and his TNT Trio."

And so it went, night after night. I'll confess that I was a stranger to the Phi Beta Kappa selection board, but nonetheless, my grades were adequate. I got by, and whatever happened in my classes, I had the comfort of knowing that I was becoming a well-rounded-out personality. Some nights I could actually feel my personality rounding out—like a balloon.

But occasionally a doubt would dart through my mind like a lizard across a rock. Then I would say to myself, "This can't go on forever." I found out I was right one morning in my English class.

On that morning at the end of the class hour, our instructor, Mr. Hambrick, announced, "There will be a five-hundred-word theme due next Friday. Write about any subject you want to. No excuses will be accepted for late themes. Class dismissed."

The heart within me sank. I had long been worried about Mr. Hambrick. Mr. Hambrick was one of those college English instructors who had taken a teaching job thirty years before so they could have an income while they worked on their novels. Now they were still teaching English and they were still on the first chapters of their novels. They vented their frustration on their students.

Up to this assignment I had managed to get along in Mr. Hambrick's class. Before this I had had to turn in three or four book reports, all of which Clothilde supplied from the *Book Review Digest*. But a theme was different. You can't go about clipping original themes from other sources.

"Clothilde," I said that evening, "I'm afraid the movies are out for tonight. I've got to turn in a theme for English on Friday and here it is Tuesday and I'd better get to work."

"But, Dobie," wailed Clothilde. "It's Montgomery Clift. He knocks me out. Doesn't he knock you out?"

"No," I said truthfully. "Listen, Clothilde, I'd better do this theme. This isn't the kind of thing I can chisel on. I've got to do it myself, and I'd better get started."

"How long does it have to be?"

"Five hundred words."

"What's the topic?"

"Anything I want."

"Well, then, what's your hurry? It's only Tuesday. You've got Wednesday and Thursday to work on it."

"No, I'd better start it right away. I don't know whether I can finish it all in one night. Don't forget, Clothilde, I'm not very bright."

"Yes, I know," she said, "but even *you* should be able

to write a five-hundred-word theme in one night. Especially if you can pick your own subject."

"Look, Clothilde, I don't want to seem stubborn, but I've made up my mind. I'm going to start that theme tonight and that's final."

"Shelley Winters is in the picture too."

"Let's hurry so we can get good seats," I said.

The next night, Wednesday, I was positively going to work on the theme. *Positively.* But Benny Goodman was playing a one-night stand at the Auditorium, and, as Clothilde said, "You can't just not go to hear Benny Goodman. How will you explain it to people?"

And Thursday afternoon there was a Sunlite Dance in the Union with a jitterbug contest for which Clothilde and I had been rehearsing for weeks. Unfortunately, Clothilde threw a shoe and pulled up lame at the end of the second lap and we had to drop out.

Not until six o'clock Thursday evening did I get to the theme. I set two fountain pens, a bottle of ink, an eraser, three pencils, a dictionary, a thesaurus, and a ream of fresh white paper on my desk. I adjusted the goose-neck lamp for minimum eyestrain. I pulled up a straight-back chair. I opened the window. I filled a pitcher with water, I took my phone off the hook. Then I sat down and drew isosceles triangles for two hours.

Not an idea came to me. Not a fragment of an idea. Not a teensy-weensy glimmer of an idea. I had just about decided to drop out of the university and enroll in a manual-training school when I heard Clothilde calling me outside my window.

I stuck my head out. "How ya doin', Dobie?" she asked.

I grimaced.

"I thought so," she said. "Well, don't worry. I've got it all figured out. Look." She held up two white cards.

"What's that?" I asked.

"Stack permits," she replied.

"What?"

"Come on out and I'll explain the whole thing."

"Listen, Clothilde, I don't know what you're up to, but I don't want any part of it. I'm going to sit here all night if I have to, but I'm going to finish that theme. I don't care what you say; there's no other way to do it."

"Come on out, you jerk. I've never failed you yet, have I? Listen, you'll not only have your theme written tonight, but we'll be able to catch the last feature at the Bijou."

"No."

"You don't really believe you're going to get that theme written, do you?"

She had me there.

"Come on out."

"What's a stack permit?" I asked.

"Come on out."

I came out.

She took my arm. "We'd better hurry, Dobie. It's after eight o'clock and the library closes at nine."

"What's that got to do with anything?"

She was pulling me along, toward the library. "Dobie, you've been to the library, haven't you?"

"I used to go occasionally," I said, "before I met you."

"All right. You know how the library works?"

"Sure," I said. "You go in and look up the book you want in the card catalogue and then you write your name and the card number of the book on a request slip and you give the slip to the librarian and she sends a page boy after your book."

"Ah," said Clothilde, "but do you know where the books come from?"

"They keep them on shelves in the back of the library."

"Stacks," said Clothilde. "Those are called stacks."

"So?"

"Ordinarily," Clothilde continued, "they don't let students go back into the stacks. They're afraid we might get the books mixed up or steal them or something. When you want a book, you turn in a request slip for it and they send a page boy after it."

"This is all very informative, Clothilde, but I wish you had picked another time to tell it to me. I've got a theme to write."

Clothilde's big blue eyes narrowed craftily into little blue eyes. "Some students, Dobie, *are* allowed to go back in the stacks. Some graduate students and a few seniors get permits. If they are doing the kind of work that requires a lot of books at hand, particularly obscure books, they can get stack permits. Then they can go back themselves and find the books they want without tying up the librarian and several page boys. These"—she waved the two white cards—"are stack permits."

"I still don't see—"

"I borrowed them," said Clothilde, "from a couple of graduate students I know. With these cards we can get into the stacks."

"But how is all this going to get my theme written?"

We were almost at the library now.

"Dobie Gillis, you dope. I swear if you didn't have freckles and a crew haircut, I'd quit going with you in a minute. Don't you understand? We're going back in the stacks and find some old book of essays that nobody has ever heard of and you'll copy one of the essays and that will be your theme."

I stopped dead. "Clothilde," I whispered, "you can't mean it."

"Why not? It's foolproof. There won't be any record of you ever having seen the book. You won't turn in a request slip for it, so nobody will be able to check back through the slips. We're going into the stacks on somebody else's permit, so you can't be checked that way. You're not going to take the book out, so there won't be a withdrawal record on your library card. I've got pencil and paper in my purse. You'll copy the essay out of the book while you're in the stacks. Then you'll put the book back exactly where you found it. Then we'll leave and nobody will be the wiser."

I sat down beside a tree in front of the library and pulled her down beside me. "Clothilde," I said, "why don't we just get a couple of revolvers and go hold up a filling station?"

"This is no time to be finicky, Dobie. You know very well you'll never get that theme written."

"True," I said after a short silence.

"Then come on into the library. It's eight-thirty."

"I can't, Clothilde. My conscience would never stop bothering me."

She pulled me to my feet. She's quite a bit stronger than I am.

"Anyway," I protested, "it's not safe. How can we be sure that Mr. Hambrick, my English instructor, hasn't read the book that I'm going to copy the essay out of?"

Clothilde smiled. "I was hoping you'd ask that question. Come along. I'll show you."

She dragged me into the library, up the stairs and to the main desk. "Stop perspiring, Dobie," she whispered. "We don't want anybody to remember us." She showed the two stack permits to the librarian. The librarian nodded us back into the stacks.

The stacks filled me with awe. They consisted of metal bookshelves arranged in banks. Each bank was seven tiers high, and each tier was six feet tall. At the head of each bank was a metal spiral staircase, wide enough for only one person. Narrow catwalks ran along each tier, and the various banks were joined by other catwalks. The whole thing, I thought, looked like the cell blocks you see in prison movies. I shuddered at the significance of the comparison.

"Come along," said Clothilde. "The essay collections are in the seventh tier of the fourth bank. Hurry. We haven't much time."

We raced through the catwalks. Our footsteps echoed metallically, and I expected to hear sirens and see spotlights at any moment. I felt like James Cagney in *White Heat*.

When we got to the essay shelves, Clothilde said,

"Now, quickly, look for a book with a lot of dust on it. Don't take any clean ones.".

We looked for a few seconds, and I found a volume gray with dust. I pulled it off the shelf. "This all right, Clothilde?"

She took it. She opened the book and looked at the record card in the envelope pasted inside the cover—the card that the library files when you take out a book. "This one is no good," said Clothilde. "The card shows that this book was last taken out in 1942. It's not very likely, but there's just a chance that your English instructor was the one who took it out. If so, he might still remember the essays. We don't have to take chances; we can find a book that hasn't been taken out for at least ten years. Then, even if your instructor was the one who checked out the book, there's not much chance that he'll remember it."

"You thought any about becoming a gun moll?" I asked.

"Hurry, Dobie, it's a quarter to nine."

We found a couple more dusty volumes, but their cards showed that they had both been out of the library within the past ten years. At seven minutes to nine, we found the right one.

"This is perfect," said Clothilde, holding up the book, a slim collection called *Thoughts of My Tranquil Hours* by one Elmo Goodhue Pipgrass. Mr. Pipgrass's picture appeared on the frontispiece—a venerable gentleman with side whiskers and a white string tie. The record card in the book was almost lily white. The book had been taken out only once, and that was 'way back in 1926.

"This is perfect," Clothilde repeated. "The book has only been taken out once. It was published"—she looked at the title page—"in 1919. The picture of Pipgrass on the frontispiece shows that he was a man of at least seventy at that time. He's certainly dead now, so you don't even have to worry about plagiarism."

"Plagiarism!" I exclaimed. "You didn't say anything about that before."

"No use to alarm you, Dobie," she said. "Hurry up now. It's five minutes to nine. Here's pencil and paper."

"Plagiarism," I muttered.

"Hurry, Dobie. For Pete's sake, hurry."

With the greatest reluctance, I took pencil and paper and began to copy the first essay in *Thoughts of My Tranquil Hours*. It started like this:

Who has not sat in the arbor of his country seat, his limbs composed, a basin of cherry russet apples at his side, his meerschaum filled with good shag; and listened to the wholesome bucolic sounds around him: the twitter of chimney swifts, the sweet piping of children at their games, the hale cries of the country-man to his oxen, the comfortable cackling of chickens, the braying of honest asses; and felt his nostrils deliciously assailed with aromas from the kitchen: the nourishing saddles of beef, the beneficent gruels, the succulent tarts; and basked in the warmth of sun and earth, full bounty of abundant nature; and thought, "Of what moment is man's travail for gain, his mad impetus toward wealth, his great unsettled yearning for he knows not what, when all about him if he would but perceive are the treasures of the globe, more precious far than any jewel which lies deep beneath virgin earth across unplumbed and perilous seas?"

That was the first sentence, and the shortest one. I scribbled furiously until I had the whole thing down, and we left. We got out of the library at five seconds before nine.

Outside, I turned on Clothilde. "Why did I ever listen to you?" I cried. "Not only do I run the risk of getting kicked out of school in disgrace, but I've got to worry about getting arrested for plagiarism too. And to top it all off, the essay stinks. He'll probably flunk me on it anyway."

"Could you have done better?" she asked.

"That's not the point—"

"Come on," she said impatiently. "We'll miss the last show at the Bijou."

I didn't enjoy the show one bit. I enjoyed even less handing in my theme on Friday morning. As I laid the sheets on Mr. Hambrick's desk, visions of policemen and hanging judges and prison gates sped through my head. My forehead was a Niagara of perspiration.

"You feel all right, Mr. Gillis?" asked Mr. Hambrick.

"Yes, sir," I said. "I feel fine, thank you."

"I was just asking," he said. "I don't really care."

The gaiety of the weekend failed to cheer me up. Dressed as a buccaneer on Saturday night, I swash-buckled listlessly through a masquerade party, and on Sunday I sat like a lump all through a hayride, never once joining in the four hundred verses of "Sweet Violets."

In my English class Monday morning I was resigned. I was prepared for the worst. I wasn't even surprised when Mr. Hambrick told me to stay behind at the end of the class.

"I want to talk to you about the theme you turned in Friday, Mr. Gillis," said Mr. Hambrick when we were alone in the room.

"Yes, sir," I said, my voice hitting high C above middle E.

"Frankly," he continued, "I was amazed at that theme. Until Friday, Mr. Gillis, I had merely thought of you as dull."

"Yes, sir."

"But now I know I was wrong. The trouble with you is that you're archaic."

"Huh?"

"You're archaic. You're way behind the times. You were born one century too late. And," he added, "so was I. I tell you, Mr. Gillis, I have no regard for modern writing. It all seems like gibberish to me—all that clipped prose, that breakneck pacing, that lean objectivity. I don't like it. I think writing should be leisurely and rich. Sentences should be long and graceful, filled with meaning and sensitive perception. Your theme, Mr. Gillis, is a perfect example of the kind of writing I most admire."

"Call me Dobie," I said genially.

"I'm going to give you an 'A' on that theme, and I hope in the future you will write some more like it."

"You bet," I said. "I know just where to get them."

"And if you're ever free on a Sunday afternoon, I'd be pleased if you'd stop at my place for a cup of tea. I'd like to talk to you about a novel I've been toying with. It's a great deal like your stuff."

"Sure, pal. Now if you'll give me my theme, I've got to get on to my next class."

"Ah," he smiled, his neutral-colored eyes twinkling behind tortoiseshell glasses, "I'm afraid I can't do that. I've got a little surprise for you, Mr. Gillis. I've entered your theme in the Minnesota Colleges Essay Contest."

I just made it to a chair. "Again," I gasped. "Say that again."

"I've entered your theme in the Minnesota Colleges Essay Contest," he repeated. "It's a competition sponsored once a year by the State Board of Education for all the colleges in Minnesota—the university and Hamline and Macalester and St. John's and all the rest. The contest is judged by the four members of the Board of Education and the winner gets a free cruise on the Great Lakes."

"Please!" I screamed. "I don't want to be in any contest. I don't want to win a Great Lakes cruise. I get seasick. Even in a bathtub I get seasick."

"Come, come, Mr. Gillis. You mustn't be so modest. Let me give you a bit of advice, my boy. I was just like you are. I hid my light beneath a bushel too. Now look at me—teaching English to a bunch of little morons. No, Mr. Gillis, you've got to assert yourself, and I'm going to see that you do."

"Please, Mr. Hambrick," I begged tearfully.

"It's too late anyhow. As soon as I read your theme last Friday night, I put it in the mail immediately. It's already in the hands of the Board of Education. The results of the contest will be announced Thursday. Well, good-bye, Mr. Gillis. I must rush to my next class."

I sat there alone in that classroom for two hours. Twitching. Just twitching. I couldn't even think. I just twitched. Like a horse dislodging flies. Then, skulking behind trees, I walked to my room, crawled into bed, and moaned until sundown.

In the evening I found Clothilde and, with a great deal of bitterness, told her the whole story.

"That's not good," said Clothilde. Sharp, that girl.

"I wish," I said honestly, "that I had never set eyes on you."

"Don't be vile, Dobie. Let's figure something out."

"Oh no you don't. I'm through listening to you. Tomorrow I'm going to Mr. Hambrick and confess everything. There's nothing else to be done, no matter what *you* say."

"Dobie, you really work hard at being stupid, don't you? That's the silliest thing I ever heard. Really, I don't see what you have to worry about. If Mr. Hambrick, a professional English instructor, didn't suspect anything, what makes you think that the members of the State Board of Education are going to get wise?"

"Now you listen to me, Clothilde. Every minute I delay my confession just makes it worse for me. It stands to reason that at least one of those Board of Education members has read Elmo Goodhue Pipgrass's *Thoughts of My Tranquil Hours*."

"Fat chance," sneered Clothilde.

"No, Clothilde. I won't do it. I know I'm going to get caught, and I might just as well get it over with."

"Honestly, I've never met such a yuck. You'll never get caught, you poor goof. They'll read the theme and reject it, and the whole business will be over with. The things you find to worry about."

"Good God, girl. What if I win the contest?"

"With that corn?" she asked. "Ha. Honestly, Dobie."

Then she argued some more, but I was firm as a rock. It took her more than twenty minutes to talk me into it.

For the next three days, as tragedy mounted on tragedy, I was numb with fear. I'll tell you how numb I was: a practical joker in my political science class put a tack on my seat and I sat on it all through the class.

Tuesday Mr. Hambrick said to me, "Good news, Mr. Gillis. Your essay has advanced into the quarter-finals."

I nodded mutely and went out into the hall and twitched some more.

Wednesday Mr. Hambrick said to me, "Great news, Mr. Gillis. Your essay is now in the semi-finals."

I tried to confess everything to him then, but all that came out of my throat were hoarse croaks.

And Thursday the walls came tumbling down.

"Mr. Gillis," said Mr. Hambrick, "Something very curious has happened. Your essay won out in the semi-finals and was entered in the finals. Your competition in the finals was an essay by a young man named Walter Bradbury from Macalester College. Mr. Bradbury's essay is a description of iron mining in northern Minnesota. Now, it happens that of the four members of the Board of Education, two are from the Iron Range district. Those two insist on awarding the prize to Mr. Bradbury. But the other two members want to give you the prize. Neither side will yield."

"I'll withdraw," I said hastily.

"That's noble of you," said Mr. Hambrick, "but it won't be necessary. The Board of Education has agreed to call in an impartial judge to pick the winner. You and Mr. Bradbury are to go over to the Board of Education office in the state capitol this afternoon for the final judging. I've arranged transportation for you."

"Mr. Hambrick," I pleaded desperately. "Let them

give the prize to Bradbury. The sea air will do him good."

"Nonsense," Mr. Hambrick laughed. "You're sure to win. I know the judge they picked is going to favor you. He's a distinguished essayist himself, who used to write much as you do. He's been in retirement for many years at a cottage near Lake Minnetonka. He's very old. Possibly you may have heard of him. His name is Elmo Goodhue Pipgrass."

Click. I heard a distinct click in my head. Then a terrifying calm came over me. I felt drained of emotion, no longer capable of fear or worry. I felt as a man must feel who is finally strapped into the electric chair.

"There will be a car in front of the Administration Building in thirty minutes to take you to the state capitol," said Mr. Hambrick.

"Yes, sir," I said. My voice seemed to be coming from far away.

"Good luck—Dobie."

I found Clothilde and told her everything—told it to her evenly, coolly, without rancor.

"I'm going to the state capitol with you," she said. "I'll think of something."

I patted her shoulder. "Thank you, Clothilde, but no. It will be better if we break clean—now. I don't want you to be known as the consort of a criminal. Your whole life is ahead of you, Clothilde. I don't want to be a burden to you. Try to forget me, Clothilde, if you can. Find somebody new."

"You're awfully sweet, Dobie."

"And so are you, Clothilde, in an oblique way."

"Then this—this is it?"

"Yes, Clothilde. This," I said, the little muscles in my jaw rippling, "is it."

"What are you going to do with those two tickets to Tommy Dorsey tonight?"

"They're yours, Clothilde." I handed them to her and added with a wry smile, "I won't be needing them."

We shook hands silently, and I went off to the

Administration Building and got into the car and was
driven to the state capitol.

I went into the Board of Education office and was
directed to the conference room. This room contained
a long mahogany table with five empty chairs behind
it. There were two chairs in front of the table, and in
one of them sat a young man wearing a sweater with
"Macalester" emblazoned across the front.

"You must be Walter Bradbury." I said. "I'm Dobie
Gillis."

"Hi," he said. "Sit down. They'll be here in a minute."

I sat down. We heard footsteps in the hall.

"Here they come," said Bradbury. "Good luck,
Dobie."

"Oh no, no, no!" I cried. "Good luck to you. I want
you to win. With all my heart I do. Nothing would
make me happier."

"Why, thanks. That's awfully decent of you."

They came in, and the pit of my stomach was a
roaring vastness. The four members of the Board of
Education were dressed alike in dark business suits and
looked alike—all plumpish, all bespectacled, all bald-
ing. With them, carrying a gnarled walking stick, was
Elmo Goodhue Pipgrass, the littlest, oldest man I had
ever seen. His side whiskers were white and wispy, the
top of his head egg-bald. His eyes looked like a pair of
bright shoe buttons. He wore a high collar with a
black string tie, a vest with white piping, and congress
gaiters. He was ninety-five if he was a day.

One of the Board members took Pipgrass's arm to
assist him. "Take your big fat hand off my arm,"
roared Pipgrass. "Think I'm a baby? Chopped half a
cord of wood this morning, which is more than you
ever chopped in your whole life. Weaklings. The
government is full of weaklings. No wonder the country's gone to rack and ruin. Where are the boys?"

"Right over here, Mr. Pipgrass," said a Board member, pointing at Bradbury and me. "See them?"

"Of course I see them. Think I'm blind? Impudence

from public servants. What's the world come to? Howdy, boys." He nodded vigorously at a hall tree. "Sit down."

"They are sitting down, Mr. Pipgrass," said a Board member. "Over here."

"Whippersnapper," muttered Pipgrass. "I remember when they built this state capitol. Used to come and watch 'em every day. If I'd known they were going to fill it with whippersnappers, I'd have dynamited it."

"Mr. Pipgrass," said a member gently, "let's get to the essays. The boys have to get back to school."

"Essays? What you talking about? I haven't written an essay since 1919."

Suddenly hope was reborn within me. The man was senile. Maybe I'd get away with it. Maybe . . .

"The boys' essays, Mr. Pipgrass. You're to pick the best one, remember?"

"Certainly, I remember. Think I'm an idiot? Who's Bradbury?"

"I, sir," said Bradbury.

"Ah. You're the fool who wrote an essay on iron mining. Iron mining! Why didn't you write one on plumbing? Or garbage disposal?"

I felt a sinking sensation.

"Or roofing?" continued Pipgrass. "Or piano tuning? Iron mining! What kind of subject is that for an essay? And furthermore you split four infinitives. And don't you know that a compound sentence takes a comma between clauses? Great Jehoshaphat, boy, where'd you ever get the idea you could write?"

Bradbury and I trembled, each for his own reason.

"Gillis," said Pipgrass. "Gillis, you pompous, mealy-mouthed little hack. Who told you that you were a writer?" He picked up my essay, held it a half-inch before his face, and read, " 'Who has not sat in the arbor of his country seat . . .' " He threw down the essay. "I'll tell you who has not sat in the arbor of his country seat. You haven't. Bradbury hasn't. All of these four fat fellows haven't. Who the devil has got a country seat? What the devil *is* a country seat? Who talks about country seats these days? What kind of writer are you? Who said you were a writer? Can't anybody write in this confounded state?

"It's a sorry choice," said Pipgrass, "that I have to make between these two wights. Neither of 'em can write worth a nickel. But if I must choose, give the prize to Bradbury."

A great weight rolled off my back. A film dropped from my eyes. I smiled a real smile.

Now they were all around Bradbury shaking his hand, but none so heartily as I. I waited until they all left the room and then I got down on my knees and sent off six quick prayers. I mopped my forehead, my cheeks, my chin, my neck, and my palms, and then I went into the hall.

Pipgrass was waiting for me.

"You Gillis?" he asked.

I nodded, holding the doorjamb for support.

He took my arm. "I was tempted to give you the prize, boy. Mighty flattering to know that people are still reading *Thoughts of My Tranquil Hours* after all these years."

Then he was gone down the corridor, chuckling and running his walking stick across the radiators.

Jean Kerr
[1923–   ]

Jean Kerr is an outstanding humorist of American domestic life. She directs her wit at the comic commonplaces of marriage and family, and especially at contemporary woman's roles as wife, mother, and career woman—roles which she herself has juggled expertly. She is the mother of six children, a playwright with several Broadway successes to her credit (including collaborations with her husband, drama critic Walter Kerr), the author of the bestselling novel *Please Don't Eat the Daisies,* and a frequent contributor to leading magazines.

I JUST STEPPED OUT OF <u>VOGUE</u>

Last spring I saw a play called *And Things That Go Bump in the Night*. I won't tell you the plot. But it was about this young man who was so disturbed that he turned up in the second act wearing a dress.

I don't know what he was disturbed about. But I know what I was disturbed about. He was wearing my dress. I mean the one I had on. There it was, the same check, the same little piqué collar, the same dreary buttons down the front. Except for the fact that I wear my hair shorter and I'm getting quite gray, we could have been twins.

My first instinct was to flee the premises immediately, perhaps on the pretext that I was suffering appendicitis pains. (After all, it is not widely known that I have already parted with my appendix.) But it occurred to me that if I dashed up the center aisle looking precisely like the leading man I might be regarded as part of the entertainment. So I just slouched down into my seat and pressed my purse up under my chin in the hope of covering at least the collar of that wretched dress. Thereafter I just waited until the entire audience had dispersed before I crept out under cover of darkness.

The incident left its mark on me. But it did serve to clear up an episode that had always been something of a mystery. Two years earlier I had been standing in the lobby of a hotel in Venice. Right next to me, waiting for her key, was a woman I recognized as the celebrated couturière Valentina. I noticed that she was looking exquisite in beige linen. I also noticed that she was staring at me in some perplexity. It was as though she were mentally snapping her fingers.

Thinking I understood the situation, I said, "Madame Valentina, we've never met, but my husband reviews plays and I see you very often at opening nights." And I told her my name. She smiled, and said very quietly, "Oh, I *knew* the name."

I didn't have the wit, or perhaps I didn't have the heart, to ask the next question: "What didn't you know?" So we bowed and parted gravely. Of course, it's all clear enough to me now. I was wearing that same damn brown check dress, with—oh, my God—blue tennis shoes. And Madame Valentina was asking herself "Where did she buy it? When? Why?"

Well, that's what happens when you try to hobnob. As for that particular dress, I have already taken a garden rake and some matches and burned it in the driveway. But the question remains: Why *do* I have all these horrible golfing-type dresses when, for one thing, I don't even golf? It's true that I am tall and hard to fit, but I don't think the salesladies I get even try. At the first sight of me they smile wanly (as though greeting the recently bereaved), waggle their heads, and say, "Oh, I'm afraid I wouldn't have a thing."

Now how can they tell that when I haven't even taken off my coat? Eventually, they brighten up just enough to ask, "Has Madam tried our sportswear section?" Passing the buck is what I call it. Anyway, that's my problem. I've been trying the sportswear section for twenty years.

Other women arrange their wardrobes with such *élan*. I have read that Mrs. Michelene Lerner keeps life-sized foam-rubber models of her figure in various fashion houses in Rome, Paris, London, and New York. Then, if she sees a picture of a dress she admires, she doesn't even have to go in for a fitting. She can just call London or Paris and order it. I think this is a marvelous plan. And the reason I haven't had a dozen foam-rubber models made of my figure is not just that there isn't enough foam rubber in the world. The real reason I'm hesitant is that I don't think a life-sized foam-rubber model of me could be stashed away in a closet someplace, between fittings. It would absolutely require a proper setting. It would have to be placed like Michelangelo's David—in a rotunda, with perhaps a skylight. Now, I have never been in a fashion house but I doubt if they have rotundas. Also, I have the feeling that it would be rather depressing to have oneself duplicated all over the place. Imagine trying to eat some *crème-brûlée* and realizing that you were getting fat in four different cities.

Mignon McLaughlin has written that a woman can remember exactly what she was wearing on every important occasion of her life. I believe that. I can remember. I just wish I could forget. Because even when I find a dress that is pretty and becoming, it turns out, in one way or another, to be a mistake. Let me give you a typical example.

Years ago, when my husband first went to work on a newspaper, we were invited to a dinner party by the man who was then the managing editor. Now I didn't really suppose my husband would be fired if I should prove unsuitable (I don't think newspapers worry about their "image" the way corporations do) but I did suppose that I couldn't appear at a chic dinner party in a dress that buttoned down the front. I knew I had to take steps.

I went to Lord & Taylor and bravely marched into "Better Dresses." Then I stood in a corner for a while and studied the salesladies. What I did *not* want was an elegant saleslady. I knew, from past experience, that in the presence of a really elegant saleslady with a really elegant European accent I tend to drop my purse and my gloves and to develop coughing spells.

I finally selected one who seemed a little shy and nervous. I went over to her and took hold of her elbow. "Don't *argue* with me," I said, "I want to buy a dress. I want to buy a fancy dress. And I want to buy it this afternoon." She didn't seem startled by my outburst. She just sighed a little sigh that seemed to say "Boy,

I get all the nuts!" Then she went to work and found me a pretty dress. It was made of yellow silk pongee with metallic gold thread woven through the fabric. And so I went to the party calm in my conviction that for once I was wearing something that did not look as though it had been run up by loving hands at home.

My husband and I were the first to arrive because we had made the youthful error of arriving at precisely the time for which we had been invited. The editor and his wife greeted us in the foyer and were most gracious. I felt, however, that the wife's smile was a little bit strained. I understood everything when we walked into the living room. Three walls of the room were covered from floor to ceiling with draperies. And the draperies were made of exactly the same material as my new dress. What depressed me most was my feeling that I *wouldn't* die of embarrassment.

I tried to appraise the overall situation. It wasn't so terrible. It just looked as though they'd had enough material left over to make a dress. But then why, in heaven's name, would I be wearing it? Actually, it didn't matter so much to me that when I was standing in front of a drapery I seemed to be a disembodied head. It mattered more to the other guests, who were hard put to analyze what they assumed must be an optical illusion. Conversations with me had a way of sputtering out. In fact, one man left my side in the middle of a sentence muttering, "I don't know *what* they put in this drink." Finally, I had to devote all of my energies to keeping near the one undraped—or safe —wall, where the heat from the open fireplace promptly took the curl out of my hair. Needless to say, we were not invited back.

Another reason I have so many dreary dresses is that I *know* I am a difficult size, which means that whenever a saleslady produces a dress that actually fits me I feel a sporting obligation to buy it. (I consider a dress fits me when it reaches to my knees and can be zipped up by only one person.) I seem unable to make plain statements like "I can't wear beige because I *am* beige." I may venture a feeble question, "Don't you think it's a little on the beige side?", but if I do the saleslady instantly counters with "Madam must imagine it dressed up with spanking white accessories." So naturally I buy the dress. I'm certainly not going to confess to that girl that I don't own one single spanking white accessory.

By contrast, my mother has great authority in these situations. I once went shopping with her when she was looking for a dress to wear to my brother's wedding. The saleslady brought out a somber mauve lace with that ubiquitous rhinestone pin on the hip. Mother waved it away. The saleslady turned frosty on the instant and asked, "Would you care to tell me what you don't like about it?" Mother smiled cheerily and said, "My dear, all my friends are being *buried* in that dress." She got results, and a very becoming gray chiffon, in ten minutes.

There is this to be said for my ill-purchased dresses. They are, almost invariably, of such stout material and such sturdy construction that it gives me a very good feeling when I pack them off to the Clothes for Korea collection. Some people are denied even this small comfort. I have a friend, a very pretty girl named Margaret Mary who, in spite of the fact that her weight fluctuates wildly (that is to say, she keeps getting fatter) continues to buy chic clothes at fashionable boutiques. Of course she can't wear them. And she tells me that when she opens her closet doors it gives her the sensation of drowning. It's as though all the sins of her past life were swimming before her eyes.

The question is: What do you do with a closet full of unused velvet Capri pants or sequined bekinis? These cannot be dispatched to the deserving poor. Indeed, they don't even make good dusters. They just hang there, a reminder of the folly of human aspirations and the futility of nine-day diets.

Art Buchwald
[1925–   ]

Art Buchwald is one of America's most popular columnists. He began his career in Paris, where he arrived in 1948 as a correspondent for *Variety*, and later worked for the European edition of the *New York Herald Tribune*. After fourteen years, he returned to the United States and settled in Washington. His column for the *Washington Post* is now syndicated worldwide and enjoyed by millions of readers. Buchwald's sharply perceptive political satire is matched by his ability to penetrate the obvious in every area, revealing the ludicrous in current events and social trends. His columns have been collected in several books, including *I Never Danced at the White House* and *Washington Is Leaking*.

FRESH AIR WILL KILL YOU

Smog, which was once the big attraction of Los Angeles, can now be found all over the country from Butte, Montana to New York City, and people are getting so used to polluted air that it's very difficult for them to breathe anything else.

I was lecturing recently, and one of my stops was Flagstaff, Arizona, which is about 7,000 miles above sea level.

As soon as I got out of the plane, I smelled something peculiar.

"What's that smell?" I asked the man who met me at the plane.

"I don't smell anything," he replied.

"There's a definite odor that I'm not familiar with," I said.

"Oh, you must be talking about the fresh air. A lot of people come out here who have never smelled fresh air before."

"What's it supposed to do?" I asked suspiciously.

"Nothing. You just breathe it like any other kind of air. It's supposed to be good for your lungs."

"I've heard that story before," I said. "How come if it's air, my eyes aren't watering?"

"Your eyes don't water with fresh air. That's the advantage of it. Saves you a lot in paper tissues."

I looked around and everything appeared crystal clear. It was a strange sensation and made me feel very uncomfortable.

My host, sensing this, tried to be reassuring. "Please

don't worry about it. Tests have proved that you can breathe fresh air day and night without its doing any harm to the body."

"You're just saying that because you don't want me to leave," I said. "Nobody who has lived in a major city can stand fresh air for a very long time. He has no tolerance for it."

"Well, if the fresh air bothers you, why don't you put a handkerchief over your nose and breathe through your mouth?"

"Okay, I'll try it. If I'd known I was coming to a place that had nothing but fresh air, I would have brought a surgical mask."

We drove in silence. About fifteen minutes later he asked, "How do you feel now?"

"Okay, I guess, but I sure miss sneezing."

"We don't sneeze too much here," the man admitted. "Do they sneeze a lot where you come from?"

"All the time. There are some days when that's all you do."

"Do you enjoy it?"

"Not necessarily, but if you don't sneeze, you'll die. Let me ask you something. How come there's no air pollution around here?"

"Flagstaff can't seem to attract industry. I guess we're really behind the times. The only smoke we get is when the Indians start signaling each other. But the wind seems to blow it away."

The fresh air was making me feel dizzy. "Isn't there a diesel bus around here that I could breathe into for a couple of hours?"

"Not at this time of day. I might be able to find a truck for you."

We found a truck driver, and slipped him a five-dollar bill, and he let me put my head near his exhaust pipe for a half-hour. I was immediately revived and able to give my speech.

Nobody was as happy to leave Flagstaff as I was. My

next stop was Los Angeles, and when I got off the plane, I took one big deep breath of the smog-filled air, my eyes started to water, I began to sneeze, and I felt like a new man again.

HOW UN-AMERICAN CAN YOU GET?

I have a confession to make, and the sooner it gets out in the open, the better I'll feel about it. *I don't drive a car.*

Americans are broad-minded people. They'll accept the fact that a person can be an alcoholic, a dope fiend, a wife beater, and even a newspaperman, but if a man doesn't drive, there is something wrong with him.

Through the years I've found it very embarrassing to admit it to anyone, and my best friends tend to view me with suspicion and contempt.

But where I really run into trouble is when I go into a store and try to make a purchase with a check.

It happened again last week when I went to a discount house at a large shopping center in Maryland. I wanted to buy a portable typewriter, and the salesman was very helpful about showing me the different models.

I decided on one, and then I said, "May I write out a personal check?"

"Naturally," he said kindly. "Do you have any identification?"

"Of course," I said. I produced an American Express credit card, a Diners' Club credit card, a Carte Blanche credit card, a Bell Telephone credit card, and my pass to the White House.

The man inspected them all and then said, "Where's your driver's license?"

"I don't have one," I replied.

"Did you lose it?"

"No, I didn't lose it. I don't drive a car."

He pushed a button under the cash register, and suddenly a floor manager came rushing over.

The salesman had now become surly. "This guy's trying to cash a check, and he doesn't have a driver's license. Should I call the store detective?"

"Wait a minute. I'll talk to him," the manager said. "Did you lose your driver's license for some traffic offense?"

"No, I've never driven. I don't like to drive."

"Nobody likes to drive," the floor manager shouted. "That's no excuse. Why are you trying to cash a check if you don't have a driver's license?"

"I thought all the other identification was good enough. I had to be cleared by the Secret Service to get this White House pass," I said hopefully.

The floor manager looked scornfully at the pass and all my credit cards. "Anyone can get cleared by the Secret Service. Hey, wait a minute. How did you get out here to the shopping center if you don't drive?"

"I took a taxi," I said.

"Well, that takes the cake," he said.

By this time a crowd had gathered.

"What happened?"

"Guy doesn't have a driver's license."

"Says he doesn't even drive. Never has driven."

"Lynch him."

"Tar and feather him."

"How un-American can you get?"

The crowd was getting ugly, so I decided to forget the typewriter.

"Never mind," I said. "I'll go somewhere else."

By this time the president of the store had arrived on the scene. Fortunately, he recognized my name and okayed the check. He was very embarrassed by the treatment I had received and said, "Come on, I'll buy you a drink."

"I forgot to tell you," I said. "I don't drink either."

This was too much, even for him, and he pushed me toward the door.

"Get out of here," he said, "and don't come back!"

THE FACTS OF LIFE

This is the time of the year when fathers sit down and have heart-to-heart talks with their sons.

"Son, now that you have graduated your mother feels I would not be fulfilling my duties as a father if I did not explain certain facts about life to you."

"Yes, Dad."

"First, I would like to show you a few things that you will have to deal with in the outside world. For example, this item is called a necktie."

"What do you do with it?"

"You tie it around your neck like this and wear it with a jacket."

"What for?"

"Nobody is quite sure. But when you do go out into the cold world, people will expect you to wear one. It's the Establishment's answer to the peace symbol."

"It sure looks funny. What else, Dad?"

"This, my boy, is a suit—what are you laughing at?"

"The jacket matches the pants. Hey, that's really crazy."

"Yes, the jacket does match the pants, and you will be expected to wear them together during the daytime."

"But the pants have a crease in the front. What's that for?"

"I'm not certain of its purpose, but now that you are an adult you will be expected to keep a crease in your pants."

"Man, what will they think of next?"

"Son, I wish you wouldn't take our talk lightly. Perhaps I should have explained these things to you before, but I didn't want to ruin your school days. Yet what I am telling you now will have a great effect on everything you do."

"Sorry, Dad, but you have to admit wearing a tie and a jacket that matches the pants—what do you call it, a suit?—is a pretty funny idea."

"Can we proceed? These queer-looking leather things are called shoes. Do you have any idea what they're used for?"

"Beats me."

"You put them on your feet to protect them from sharp objects."

"I don't want to wear anything like that, Dad. I'll take my chances."

"I don't know how to break it to you, son, but most places require grown-ups to wear shoes."

"Look, Dad, if you want me to, I will wear a necktie, and I'll even go along with the jacket and matching pants with a crease in them; but I'm not going to put those stupid leather things on my feet."

"Shoes, son, shoes. Believe me, you'll get used to them. After a while you might even get to like them and keep them polished."

"You mean I have to polish them, too?"

"You don't have to, but they look better that way and last longer. Here, put on these socks and then . . ."

"What are socks?"

"You wear them under the shoes so the leather won't rub your feet."

"I thought the shoes were supposed to protect my feet."

"Provided you wear socks. Son, please don't make this too difficult for me. I'm not very good at explaining the facts of life, but believe me, I've been telling you the truth."

"I'm sorry, Dad, it's just that you've thrown all this stuff at me at one time, and it comes as a shock."

"Perhaps we've talked enough for one day. Tomorrow I'd like to tell you about a thing called a razor."

"Razor? That's a funny word."

ULCER BOOM

You're going to hear a lot about "economic indicators" this year. An economic indicator is a clue to what is really happening to the economy. From these hints economists can make fantastic predictions on which way the country will tilt in the next twelve months.

A man who works with nothing but economic indicators is Dr. Friedrich Strasser, who is in charge of the Input-Output Institute of Sensuous Economics.

A visit to Dr. Strasser's institute produced some very interesting but frightening information.

Dr. Strasser said that at the moment all his economic indicators were pointing up.

"More people are starting to travel on the airlines, which is a very good sign," he told me. "At the moment though, it's still possible to book a flight without difficulty and have a comfortable ride without people sitting on your lap. But if things keep getting better, the airports won't be able to handle the traffic, the planes will be overbooked, luggage will be lost, and the airlines will have a very good economic year."

"Wait a minute," I said. "Are you trying to say that if the economy gets better in this country, things will get worse?"

"Of course I am. Everyone knows the price of a good economy is a breakdown in services that the economy provides. The more refrigerators people buy, the less chance they have of getting them repaired. The more cars that are sold, the bigger pollution and traffic problems you have. The more the country consumes, the less opportunity there is of getting rid of the garbage."

184

Dr. Strasser said one of his best economic indicators is the behavior of shop clerks, hotel reservation people, and headwaiters.

"The nicer they are," he said, "the more trouble the country is in. During the recent recession we found shop clerks, hotel people, and headwaiters the most courteous they had been since the economic doldrums of the early sixties.

"This indicated to us that things were very bad. Lately we've been spot-checking, and we've discovered that the hotel people are getting snippety again, the clerks in stores are starting not to give a damn, and in some good restaurants the headwaiters, for the first time in two years, are becoming their old obnoxious patronizing selves. This shows that things are picking up, and the country could be in for a good year."

"It's fantastic how you people arrive at your conclusions," I said.

"It's foolproof," Dr. Strasser said. "Let's take the building industry as an example. When the country is doing badly, no one is digging up the streets or drilling steel pilings into the ground or making cement at six in the morning. People can get around easier, sleep better, and work in a quieter atmosphere.

"But as soon as the economy improves, the wreckers come out to smash down buildings, streets are barricaded by cranes, water and gas are turned off, and the noise drives everyone to the point of suicide. By just checking the nervous breakdown figures in a city for the week, we can gauge how well the building industry is doing."

"So the more anxious the country becomes, the better it is for all of us?"

"Exactly. The best economic indicators are the sales charts of the antacid stomach medicine companies. When sales of Alka-Seltzer, Bromo-Seltzer, Pepto Bismol, and Rolaids are down, this means people are content and the dollar is in trouble. But when antacid sales go up, this means people are sick and getting their faith back in the country. You can't have economic growth without ulcer growth at the same time."

"Then you're predicting a good economic year and a miserable existence for all of us?" I asked.

"Life won't be as bad as it was in the late sixties when things were booming, but I predict it will be a good enough year that people will be able to feel how miserable a healthy economy can be."

Jean Shepherd
[1929–   ]

Jean Shepherd's satiric nostalgia awakens the memories of the old and prompts recognition in the young as his characters move from one flagrantly funny situation to the next. Born in Chicago and educated at the University of Maryland and Indiana University, he has become a popular author, actor and radio personality. He has written a novel, *In God We Trust—All Others Pay Cash,* several collections of short stories, and is especially noted for his provocative and witty radio "essays" on the Public Broadcasting series "Jean Shepherd's America."

WANDA HICKEY'S NIGHT OF
GOLDEN MEMORIES

"Puberty rites in the more primitive tribal societies are
almost invariably painful and traumatic experiences."

I half dozed in front of my TV set as the speaker
droned on in his high, nasal voice. One night a week,
as a form of masochistic self-discipline, I sentence
myself to a minimum of three hours viewing educational television. Like so many other things in life,
educational TV is a great idea but a miserable reality:
murky films of home life in Kurdistan, jowly English
authors being interviewed by jowly English literary
critics, pinched-faced ladies demonstrating Japanese
brush techniques. But I watch all of it religiously—I
suppose because it is there, like Mount Everest.

"A classic example is the Ugga Buggah tribe of lower
Micronesia," the speaker continued, tapping a pointer
on the map behind him.

A shot of an Ugga Buggah teenager appeared on the
screen, eyes rolling in misery, face bathed in sweat. I
leaned forward. His expression was strangely familiar.

"When an Ugga Buggah reaches puberty, the rites
are rigorous and unvarying for both sexes. Difficult
dances are performed and the candidate for adulthood
must eat a sickening ritual meal during the postdance
banquet. You will also notice that his costume is as
uncomfortable as it is decorative."

Again the Ugga Buggah appeared, clothed in a
garment that seemed to be made of feathers and chain
mail, the top grasping his Adam's apple like an iron
clamp, his tongue lolling out in pain.

"The adults attend these tribal rituals only as chaperones and observers, and look upon the ceremony with indulgence. Here we see the ritual dance in progress."

A heavy rumble of drums; then a moiling herd of sweating feather-clad dancers of both sexes appeared on screen amid a great cloud of dust.

"Of course, we in more sophisticated societies no longer observe these rites."

Somehow, the scene was too painful for me to continue watching. Something dark and lurking had been awakened in my breast.

"What the hell you mean we don't observe puberty rites?" I mumbled rhetorically as I got up and switched off the set. Reaching up to the top bookshelf, I took down a leatherette-covered volume. It was my high school class yearbook. I leafed through the pages of photographs: beaming biology teachers, pimply-faced students, lantern-jawed football coaches. Suddenly, there it was—a sharp-etched photographic record of a true puberty rite among the primitive tribes of northern Indiana.

The caption read: "The Junior Prom was heartily enjoyed by one and all. The annual event was held this year at the Cherrywood Country Club. Mickey Eisley and his Magic Music Makers provided the romantic rhythms. All agreed that it was an unforgettable evening, the memory of which we will all cherish in the years to come."

True enough. In the gathering gloom of my Manhattan apartment, it all came back.

"You going to the prom?" asked Schwartz, as we chewed on our salami sandwiches under the stands of the football field, where we preferred for some reason to take lunch at that period of our lives.

"Yep, I guess so," I answered as coolly as I could.

"Who ya takin'?" Flick joined the discussion, sucking at a bottle of Nehi orange.

"I don't know. I was thinking of Daphne Bigelow."

I had dropped the name of the most spectacular girl in the entire high school, if not the state of Indiana itself.

"No kidding!" Schwartz reacted in a tone of proper awe and respect, tinged with disbelief.

"Yeh. I figure I'd give her a break."

Flick snorted, the gassy orange pop going down the wrong pipe. He coughed and wheezed brokenly for several moments. I had once dated Daphne Bigelow and, although the occasion, as faithful readers will recall, was not a riotous success, I felt that I was still in the running. Several occasions in the past month had led me to believe that I was making a comeback with Daphne. Twice she had distinctly acknowledged my presence in the halls between classes, once actually speaking to me.

"Oh, hi there, Fred," she had said in that musical voice.

"Uh . . . hi, Daph," I had replied wittily. The fact that my name is not Fred is neither here nor there; she had *spoken* to me. She had remembered my face from somewhere.

"Ya gotta go formal," said Schwartz. "I read on the bulletin board where it said you wear a summer formal to the prom."

"No kidding?" Flick had finished off the orange and was now fully with us. "What's a summer formal?"

"That's where you wear one of those white coats," I explained. I was known as the resident expert in our group on all forms of high life. This was because my mother was a fanatical Fred Astaire fan.

"Ya gotta rent 'em," I said with the finality of an expert.

Two weeks later, each one of us received a prim white envelope containing an engraved invitation.

The Junior Class is proud to invite you to the Junior Prom, to be held at the Cherrywood Country Club beginning eight P.M. June fifth. Dance to the music

of Mickey Eisley and his Magic Music Makers.
  Summer formal required.

                                    The Committee

It was the first engraved invitation I had ever received. The puberty rites had begun. That night around the supper table, the talk was of nothing else.

"Who ya gonna take?" my old man asked, getting right to the heart of the issue. Who you were taking to the prom was considered a highly significant decision, possibly affecting your whole life, which, in some tragic cases, it did.

"Oh, I don't know. I was thinking of a couple of girls." I replied in an offhand manner, as though this slight detail didn't concern me at all. My kid brother, who was taking all this in with sardonic interest, sneered derisively and went back to shoveling in his red cabbage. He had not yet discovered girls. My mother paused while slicing the meat loaf.

"Why not take that nice Wanda Hickey?"

"Aw, come on, Ma. This is the prom. This is important. You don't take Wanda Hickey to the *prom*."

Wanda Hickey was the only girl who I knew for an absolute fact liked me. Ever since we had been in third grade, Wanda had been hanging around the outskirts of my social circle. She laughed at my jokes and once, when we were twelve, actually sent me a valentine. She was always loitering around the tennis courts, the ball diamonds, the alleys where on long summer nights we played Kick the Can or siphoned gas to keep Flick's Chevy running. In fact, there were times when I couldn't shake her.

"Nah, I haven't decided who I'm gonna take. I was kind of thinking of Daphne Bigelow."

The old man set his bottle of Pabst Blue Ribbon down carefully on the table. Daphne Bigelow was the daughter of one of the larger men in town. There was, in truth, a street named after her family.

"You're a real glutton for punishment, ain't you?"

The old man flicked a spot of foam off the table. He was referring to an unforgettable evening I had once spent with Daphne in my callow youth. "Oh, well, you might as well learn your lesson once and for all."

He was in one of his philosophical moods. The White Sox had dropped nine straight, and a losing streak like that usually brought out his fatalistic side. He leaned back in his chair, blew some smoke toward the ceiling, and went on: "Yep. Too many guys settle for the first skirt that shows up. And regret it the rest of their lives."

Ignoring the innuendo, my mother set the mashed potatoes down on the table and said, "Well, I think Wanda is a very nice girl. But then, what I think doesn't matter."

My mother had the practiced turn of phrase of the veteran martyr, whose role in life is to suffer as publicly as possible.

"I gotta rent a summer formal," I announced.

"Christ, you gonna wear one o' them monkey suits?" the old man chuckled. He had never, to my knowledge, worn anything more formal than a sports jacket in his entire life.

"I'm going down to that place on Hohman Avenue tomorrow with Schwartz and see about it."

"Oh, boy! Lah-di-dah," said my kid brother with characteristically eloquent understatement. Like father, like son.

The next day, after school Schwartz and I went downtown to a place we both had passed countless times in our daily meanderings. Hanging out over the street was the cutout of a tall, cream-faced man dressed to the nines in high silk hat, stiff starched shirt, swallow-tailed coat, striped morning trousers, and an ivory-headed walking stick held with an easy grace by his dove-gray gloved hand. In red, sputtering neon script underneath: AL'S SWANK FORMALWEAR. RENTED BY THE DAY OR HOUR. FREE FITTINGS.

We climbed the narrow, dark wooden steps to the

second floor. Within a red arrow painted on the wall were the words SWANK FOMAL—TURN LEFT.

We went past a couple of dentists' offices and a door marked BAIL BONDSMAN—FREEDOM FOR *you* DAY OR NIGHT.

"I wonder if Fred Astaire ever comes here," Schwartz said.

"Oh, come on, Schwartz. This is serious!" I could feel excitement rising deep inside me.. The prom, the engraved invitation, the summer formal; it was all starting to come together.

Al's Swank Formalwear turned out to be a small room with a yellow light bulb hanging from the ceiling, a couple of tall glass eases containing suits on hangers, a counter and a couple of smudgy full-length mirrors, Schwartz opened negotiations with a swarthy, bald, hawk-eyed, shirt-sleeved man behind the counter. Around his neck hung a yellow measuring tape. He wore a worn vest with a half-dozen chalk pencils sticking out of the pocket.

"Uh . . . we'd like to . . . uh . . ." Schwartz began confidently.

"OK, boys. Ya wanna make it big at the prom, am I right? Ya come to the right place. Ya goin' to that hop out at Cherrywood, right?"

"Uh . . . yeah," I replied.

"And ya wanna summah fawmal, right?"

"HEY, MORTY!" he shouted out. "HERE'S TWO MORE FOR THAT BASH AT CHERRYWOOD. I'D SAY ONE THIRTY-SIX SHAWT, ONE FAWTY REGULAH." His practiced eye had immediately sized us correctly.

"COMIN' UP!" Morty's voice echoed from the bowels of the establishment.

Humming to himself, Al began to pile and unpile boxes like we weren't even there. I looked around the room at the posters of various smartly turned out men of the world. One in particular, wearing a summer formal, had a striking resemblance to Cesar Romero, his distinguished gray sideburns and bronze face contrasting nicely with the snowy whiteness of his jacket.

There was another picture, of Tony Martin, who was at that time at the peak of his movie career, usually portraying Arab princes who disguised themselves as beggars in order to make the scene at the marketplace. He was always falling in love with a slave girl who turned out to be a princess in disguise, played by Paulette Goddard. Tony's roguish grin, somewhat fly-specked, showed that he was about to break into *Desert Song*.

Schwartz was busily inspecting a collection of bow ties displayed under glass in one of the showcases.

"OK ON THE THIRTY-SIX SHAWT, AL, BUT I'M OUTA FAWTIES. HOW 'BOUT THAT FAWTY-TWO REGULAH THAT JUST CAME BACK FROM THAT DAGO WEDDING?" shouted Morty from the back room.

"CUT THE TALK AN' BRING THE GOODS!" Al shouted back, straightening up, his face flushed.

"THE FAWTY-TWO AIN'T BEEN CLEANED YET!" came from the back room.

"BRING IT OUT, AWREADY!" barked Al. He turned to me.

"This suit just come in from anotha job. Don't worry about how it looks. We'll clean it up an' take it in so's it'll fit good."

Morty emerged, a tall, thin, sad man in a gray smock, even balder than Al. He carried two suits on hangers, draped them over the counter, gave Al a dirty look and stalked back into the shadows.

"OK now, boys. First you." Al nodded to Schwartz. "Take this and try it on behind the curtain. It should fit good. It's maybe a little long at the cuffs, but we'll take them up."

Schwartz grabbed the hanger and scurried behind the green curtain. Al held up the other suit. In the middle of a dark reddish-brown stain that covered the entire right breast pocket was a neat little hole right through the jacket. Al turned the hanger around and stuck his finger through the hole.

"HEY, MORTY!" he shouted.

"WHAT NOW?"

"HOW 'BOUT THIS HOLE INNA FAWTY-TWO? CAN YA FIX IT BY TONIGHT?"

"WADDAYA WANT, MIRACLES?" Morty whined.

"Don't worry, kid. We can fix this up good as new. You'll never tell it ain't a new coat."

Schwartz emerged from the fitting room shrouded in what looked like a parachute with sleeves.

"Perfect! Couldn't be bettuh!" shouted Al exultantly, darting from behind the counter. He grabbed Schwartz by the shoulders, spun him around and, with a single movement, ran his hand up into Schwartz' crotch, measured the inseam, spun him around again, made two pencil marks on the sleeves—which came almost to his fingertips—yanked up the collar, punched him smartly in the kidney, all the while murmuring in a hoarse stage whisper:

"It's made for you. Just perfect. Couldn't be bettuh. Perfect. Like tailormade."

Schwartz smiled weakly throughout the ordeal.

"OK, kid, take it off. I'll have it ready for you next week."

Obediently, Schwartz disappeared into the fitting room. Al turned to me. "Here, slip on this coat." He held it out invitingly. I plunged my arms into its voluminous folds. I felt his iron grip on my shoulder blades as he yanked me upward and spun me around, his appraising eye darting everywhere.

"Just perfect. Couldn't be bettuh. Fits like a glove. Take it in a little here; pull in the bias here . . ."

He took out his chalk and made a few marks on my back.

"OK. Slip outa it."

Al again thrust his finger through the hole.

"Reweave it like new. An' doan worry 'bout the

stain; we'll get it out. Musta been some party. Here, try on these pants."

He tossed a pair of midnight-blue trousers over the counter at me. Inside the hot little cubicle, as I changed into the pants, I stroked the broad black-velvet stripe that lined the outer seam. I was really in the big time now. They were rumpled, of course, and they smelled strongly of some spilled beverage, but they were truly magnificent. The waist came to just a shade below my armpits, beautifully pleated. Tossing the curtain aside, I sashayed out like Cary Grant.

"Stand up straight, kid," Al breathed into my ear. An aromatic blast of pastrami and pickled herring made my head reel.

"Ah. Perfect. Just right. Put a little tuck in the waist, so." He grabbed several yards of the seat. "And a little in here." A sudden thrill of pain as he violently measured the inseam. Then it was all over.

"Now," he said, back behind his counter once again, "how do ya see the shirts? You want 'em straight or ruffled? Or pleated, maybe? Very smart." He indicated several shirts on display in his grimy glass case. "I would recommend our Monte Carlo model, a real spiffy numbah."

We both peered down at the shirts. The Monte Carlo number was, indeed, spiffy, its wide, stiff, V-cut collar arching over cascading ribbons of razor-sharp pleats.

"Boy, now that's a shirt!" Schwartz breathed excitedly.

"That what *I* want," I said aloud. No other shirt would do.

"Me, too," Schwartz seconded.

"OK now," Al continued briskly, "how 'bout studs? Ya got 'em?"

"Uh . . . what?"

He had caught me off guard. I had heard the word "stud" before, but never in a tailor shop.

"OK, I guess not. I'll throw 'em in. Because you're

high-class customers. Now, I suppose ya wanna go first-class, right?"

Al directed this question at both of us, his face assuming a look of concerned forthrightness.

"Right?" he repeated.

"Yeah." Schwartz answered uncertainly for both of us.

"I knew that the minute you two walked in. Now, I'm gonna show you somepin that is exclusive with Al's Swank Formalwear."

With an air of surreptitious mystery, he bent over, slid open a drawer and placed atop the counter an object that unfocused my eyes with its sheer kaleidoscopic brilliance.

"No place else in town can supply you with a genu-wine Hollywood paisley cummabund. It's our trademark."

I stared at the magnificent band of glowing, scintillating fabric, already seeing myself a total smash on the dance floor.

"It's only a buck extra. And worth five times the price. Adolphe Menjou always wears this model. How 'bout it, men?"

We both agreed in unison. After all, you only live once.

"Of course, included for only half a dolla more is our fawmal bow tie and matchin' booteneer. I would suggest the maroon."

"Sounds great," I answered.

"Isn't that everything?" asked Schwartz with some concern.

"Is that all! You gotta be kiddin', sonny. How do you expect to trip the light fantastic without a pair o' black patent-leatha dancin' pumps?"

"Dancin' what?" I asked.

"Shoes, shoes," he explained irritably. "And we throw in the socks for nuttin'. How 'bout it?"

"Well, uh . . ."

"Fine! So that's it, boys. I'll have everything all

ready the day before the prom. You'll really knock 'em
dead."

As we left, another loud argument broke out between
Morty and Al. Their voices accompanied us down the
long flight of narrow stairs and out into the street.

Step by step, in the ancient tradition, the tribal
ritual was being acted out. The prom, which was now
two weeks off, began to occupy our minds most of the
waking day. The semester had just about played itself
out; our junior year was almost over. The trees and
flowers were in blossom, great white clouds drifted
across deep-blue skies, and baseball practice was in full
swing—but somehow, this spring was different from
the rest. The prom was something that we had heard
about since our earliest days. A kind of golden aura
hung over the word itself. Every couple of days, the
P.A. at school announced that the prom committee
was meeting or requesting something.

There was only one thing wrong. As each day ticked
inexorably by toward that magic night at the Cherrywood Country Club, I still could not steel myself to
actually seek out Daphne Bigelow and ask her the fatal
question. Time and again, I spotted her in the halls,
drifting by on gossamer wings, her radiant complexion
casting a glow on all those around her, her brilliant
smile lighting up the corners of 202 homeroom. But
each time, I broke into a fevered sweat and chickened
out at the last instant.

The weekend before the prom was sheer torture.
Schwartz, always efficient and methodical, had already
made all his plans. We sat on the back steps of my
porch late Sunday afternoon, watching Lud Kissel next
door struggle vainly to adjust the idling speed on his
time-ravaged carburetor so that the family Nash didn't
stall at 35 miles an hour. He had been drinking, of
course, so it was quite a show.

"How ya doin' with Daphne Bigelow?" asked
Schwartz sardonically, knowing full well the answer.

"Oh, that. I haven't had time to ask her," I lied.

"Ya better get on the stick. There's only a week left."

"Who *you* got lined up?" I asked, tossing a pebble at old Lud, who was now asleep under his running board.

"Clara Mae Mattingly," Schwartz replied in a steady, expressionless voice.

I was surprised. Clara Mae was one of those shadowy, quiet girls who rarely were mentioned outside of honor rolls and stuff like that. She wore gold-rimmed glasses and still had pigtails.

"Yep," Schwartz added smugly, gratified by my reaction.

"Boy, she sure can spell." It was all I could think of to say that was good about her, other than the fact that she was female.

"Sure can," Schwartz agreed. He, too, had been quite a speller in our grade school days; and on more than one occasion, Clara Mae had demolished him with a brilliant display of virtuosity in a school-wide spell-down, a form of verbal Indian wrestling now almost extinct but which at one time was a Waterloo for many of us among the unlettered. Clara Mae had actually once gone to the state finals and had lost out to a gangly farm girl from downstate who apparently had nothing else to do down there but read *Webster's* through the long winter nights.

"You gonna send her a corsage?" I asked.

"Already ordered it. At the Cupid Florist." Schwartz' self-satisfaction was overflowing.

"An orchid?"

"Yep. Cost eight bucks."

"Holy God! Eight bucks!" I was truly impressed.

"That includes a gold pin for it."

Our conversation trailed off as Lud Kissel rose heavily to his knees and crawled off down the driveway on all fours, heading for the Bluebird Tavern, which was closed on Sundays. Lud always got restless in the spring.

A few hours later, after supper, I went out gloomily

to water the lawn, a job that purportedly went toward
earning my allowance, which had reached an all-time
high that spring of three dollars a week. Fireflies played
about the cottonwoods in the hazy twilight, but I was
troubled. One week to go; less, now, because you
couldn't count the day of the prom itself. In the
drawer where I kept my socks and scout knife, buried
deep in the back, were twenty-four one-dollar bills,
which I had saved for the prom. Just as deep in my
cowardly soul, I knew I could never ask Daphne
Bigelow to be my date.

Refusing to admit it to myself, I whistled moodily
as I sprayed the irises and watched a couple of low-
flying bats as they skimmed over the lawn and up into
the poplars. Mrs. Kissel, next door, creaked back and
forth on her porch swing, a copy of *True Romances*
open in her lap, as she waited for Lud's return with his
usual snootful. My kid brother came out onto the
porch and, from sheer habit, I quickly shot a stream of
water over him, catching him in mid-air as he leaped
high to avoid the stream. It was a superbly executed
shot. I had led him just right. He caught it full in the
chest, his yellow polo shirt clinging to his ribs wetly,
like a second skin. Bawling at the top of his lungs, he
disappeared into the house and slammed the screen
door behind him. Ordinarily, this small triumph would
have cheered me up for hours; but tonight, I tasted
nothing but ashes. Suddenly, his face reappeared in
the doorway.

"I'M GONNA TELL MA!" he yelled.

Instantly, like a cobra, I struck. Sweeping the stream
quickly over the screen door, I got him again. Another
scream of rage and he was gone. Again, I sank into
my moody sea of reflection. Was I going to boot the
prom?

Flick had asked Janie Hutchinson, a tall, funny girl
who had been in our class since kindergarten. And
Schwartz was lined up with Clara Mae; all he had
talked about that week had been that crummy orchid

and how good a dancer he was. Flick had stopped asking me about Daphne ever since the past Wednesday, when I had gotten mad because he'd been needling me. All week, I had been cleaning up my Ford for the big night. If there was one thing in my life that went all the way, my only true and total love, it was my Ford V8, a convertible that I had personally rebuilt at least 35 times. I knew every valve spring personally, had honed each valve, burnished every nut and bolt she carried. Tuesday, I had simonized her completely; Wednesday, I had repeated the job; and Thursday, I had polished the chrome until my knuckles ached and my back was stiff. I had spent the past two days minutely cleaning the interior, using a full can of saddle soap on the worn leather. Everything was set to go, except for one thing—no girl.

A feeling of helpless rage settled over me as I continued spraying the lawn. I flushed out a poor, hapless caterpillar from under a bush, squirting him mercilessly full blast, until he washed down the sidewalk and disappeared into the weeds. I felt a twinge of evil satisfaction as he rolled over and over helplessly. It was getting dark. All that was left of the sun was a long purple-orange streak along the western horizon. The glow of the steel mills to the north and east began to light up the twilight sky. I had worked my way down to the edge of our weedy, pock-marked bed of sod when, out of the corner of my eye, I noticed something white approaching out of the gloom. I sprinkled on, not knowing that another piece was being fitted into the intricate mosaic of adolescence. I kicked absentmindedly at a passing toad as I soaked down the dandelions.

"What are you doing?"

So deeply was I involved in self-pity that at first my mind wouldn't focus. Startled, I swung my hose around, spraying the white figure on the sidewalk ten feet away.

"I'm sorry!" I blurted out, seeing at once that I had washed down a girl dressed in white tennis clothes.

"Oh, hi, Wanda. I didn't see you there."

She dried herself with a Kleenex.

"What are you doing?" she asked again.

"I'm sprinkling the lawn." The toad hopped past, going the other way now. I squirted him briefly, out of general principles.

"You been playing tennis?" Since she was wearing tennis clothes and was carrying a racket, it seemed the right thing to say.

"Me and Eileen Akers were playing. Down at the park," she answered.

Eileen Akers was a sharp-faced, bespectacled girl I had, inexplicably, been briefly in love with in the third grade. I had come to my senses by the time we got into 4-B. It was a narrow escape. By then, I had begun to dimly perceive that there was more to women than being able to play a good game of Run Sheep, Run.

"I'm sure glad school's almost over," she went on, when I couldn't think of anything to say. "I can hardly wait. I never thought I'd be a senior."

"Yeah," I said.

"I'm going to camp this summer. Are you?"

"Yeah," I lied. I had a job already lined up for the summer, working for a surveyor. The next camp I would see would be in the Ozarks, and I'd be carrying an M-1.

Wanda swung her tennis racket at a June bug that flapped by barely above stall speed. She missed. The bug soared angrily up and whirred off into the darkness.

"Are you going to college when you graduate next year?" she asked. For some reason, I didn't like the drift of the conversation.

"Yeah, I guess so, if I don't get drafted."

"My brother's in the Army. He's in the Artillery." Her brother, Bud Hickey, was a tall, laconic type four or five years older than both of us.

"Yeah, I heard. Does he like it?"

"Well, he doesn't write much," she said. "But he's gonna get a pass next September, before he goes overseas."

"How come he's in the Artillery?" I asked.

"I don't know. They just put him there. I guess because he's tall."

"What's that gotta do with it? Do they have to *throw* the shells, or something?"

"I don't know. They just did it."

Then it happened. Without thinking, without even a shadow of a suspicion of planning, I heard myself asking: "You going to the prom?"

For a long instant she said nothing, just swung her tennis racket at the air.

"I guess so," she finally answered, weakly.

"It's gonna be great," I said, trying to change the subject.

"Uh . . . who are you going with?" She said it as if she really didn't care one way or the other.

"Well, I haven't exactly made up my mind yet." I bent down unconcernedly and pulled a giant milkweed out by the roots.

"Neither have I," she said.

It was then that I realized there was no sense fighting it. Some guys are born to dance forever with the Daphne Bigelows on shining ballroom floors under endless starry skies. Others—well, they do the best they can. I didn't know that yet, but I was beginning to suspect something.

"Wanda?"

"Yes?"

"Wanda. Would you . . . well . . . I mean . . . would you, you see, I was thinking . . ."

"Yes?"

Here I go, in over the horns: "Wanda, uh . . . how about . . . going to the prom with me?"

She stopped twitching her tennis racket. The crickets cheeped, the spring air was filled with the sound of singing froglets. A soft breeze carried with it the promise of a rich summer and the vibrant aromas of a nearby refinery.

She began softly, "Of course, I've had a lot of invitations, but I didn't say yes to any of them yet. I guess it would be fun to go with you," she ended gamely.

"Yeah, well, naturally, I've had four or five girls who wanted to go with me, but I figured that they were mostly jerks anyway, and . . . ah . . . I meant to ask you all along."

The die was cast. There was no turning back. It was an ironclad rule. Once a girl was asked to the prom, only a total crumb would ever consider ducking out of it. There had been one or two cases in the past, but the perpetrators had become social pariahs, driven from the tribe to fend for themselves in the unfriendly woods.

Later that night, hunched over the kitchen table, still somewhat numbed by the unexpected turn of events, I chewed thoughtfully on a peanut-butter-and-jelly sandwich, while my mother, hanging over the sink in her rump-sprung Chinese-red chenille bathrobe, droned on monotonously: "You're just going to *have* to stop squirting Randy."

"Yeah," I answered, my mind three light-years away.

"You got his new Flash Gordon T-shirt all wet."

"Sorry," I said automatically. It was a phrase I used often in those days.

"It shrunk. And now he can't wear it."

"Why not?" I asked.

"It comes up around his chest now."

"Well, why can't he stretch it?"

"You just stop squirting him, that's all. You hear me?"

"It's a silly T-shirt, anyway," I said truculently.

"You heard what I said. No more squirting." That ended the conversation.

Later, in bed, I thought briefly of Daphne Bigelow, but was interrupted by a voice from the bed on the other side of the room.

"You rotten crumb. You squirted my T-shirt!"

"Ah, shaddup."

"You wait. I'm gonna get you!"

I laughed raucously. My kid brother wailed in rage. "SHUT UP, YOU TWO! CUT OUT THE FIGHT-ING OR I'LL COME IN THERE AND DO SOME HEAD KNOCKING!"

The old man meant what he said and we knew it. I promptly fell asleep. It had been a long and tumultuous day.

I broke the news to Schwartz the next morning, after biology. We were hurrying through the halls between classes on our way to our lockers, which were side by side on the second floor.

"Hey, Schwartz, how about double-dating for the prom?" I asked. I knew he had no car and I needed moral support, anyway.

"Great! I'll help you clean up the car."

"I've already simonized her. She's all set."

"Are you gonna send Daphne an orchid, or what?"

"Well, no . . ." I said lamely, hoping he'd forget what he asked.

"What do you mean? Ya gotta send a corsage."

"Well, I *am* going to send a corsage."

"I thought you said you weren't."

I just couldn't shake him off. "I never said I wasn't gonna send a corsage."

"Are you nuts? You just said you weren't gonna."

"I'm not gonna send a corsage to Daphne Bigelow. You asked me if I was gonna send a corsage to Daphne. I'm not."

"She's gonna think you're a real cheapskate."

It was getting ridiculous. Schwartz was being even more of a numskull than usual.

"Schwartz, I have decided not to ask Daphne Bigelow to the prom."

He looked directly at me, which caused him to slam into two strolling freshman girls. Their books slid across the floor, where they were trampled underfoot by the thundering mob.

"Well, who *are* you taking?" he asked, oblivious to their shrieks of dismay.

"Wanda Hickey."

"*Wanda Hickey!*"

Schwartz was completely thrown by the bit of news. Wanda Hickey had never been what you could call a major star in our Milky Way. We walked on, saying nothing, until finally, as we opened our lockers, Schwartz said: "Well, she sure is good at algebra."

It was true. Wanda was an algebra shark in the same way that Clara Mae was a spelling nut. Maybe we both got what we deserved.

Later that day, in the study hall, after I had polished off a history theme on some stupid thing like the Punic Wars, I got to thinking about Wanda. I could see her sitting way over on the other side of the room, a dusty sunbeam filtering through the window and lighting up her straw-colored hair. She was kind of cute. I'd never really noticed it before. Ever since second grade, Wanda had just been there, along with Eileen Akers, Helen Weathers, and all the other girls who—along with me and Schwartz and Flick and Jossway and the rest—had moved together step by step up the creaky ladder of education. And here I was, at long last, taking Wanda Hickey—*Wanda Hickey*—to the prom, the only junior prom I would ever attend in my life.

As I chewed on the end of my fake-marble Wear-ever pen, I watched Wanda through half-closed eyes in the dusty sunbeam as she read *The Lady of the Lake*. Ahead of me, Schwartz dozed fitfully, as he always did in study hall, his forehead occasionally thumping the desk. Flick, to my right, struggled sullenly over his chemistry workbook. We both knew it was hopeless. Flick was the only one in our crowd who consistently flunked everything.

The prom was just five days away. This was the last week of school. Ahead our long summer in the sun stretched out like a lazy yellow road. For many of us, it was the last peaceful summer we were to know.

Mr. Wilson, the study-hall teacher, wandered aimlessly up and down the aisles, pretending he was interested in what we were pretending to be doing. From somewhere outside drifted the cries of a girls' volleyball game, while I drew pictures of my Ford on the inside cover of my three-ring notebook: front view, side view, rear view, outlining the drawing with ink.

That morning, on my way to school, I had gone down to the Cupid Florist Shop and ordered an orchid. My twenty-four dollars were shrinking fast. The eight-dollar bite for the orchid didn't help. Schwartz and I were going to split on the gas, which would come to maybe a buck apiece. After paying for the summer formal I'd have a fast ten dollars left for the night. As I sat in study hall, I calculated, writing the figures down, adding and subtracting. But it didn't come out to much, no matter how I figured it.

Schwartz passed a note back to me. I opened it: "How about the Red Rooster afterward?"

I wrote underneath, "Where else?" and passed it back. The Red Rooster was part of the tribal ritual. It was *the* place you went after a big date, if you could afford it.

I glanced over across the room at Wanda and caught her looking at me. She instantly buried her head in her book. Good old Wanda.

On the way home from school every day that week of course, all we talked about was the prom. Flick was double-dating with Jossway and we were all going to meet afterward at the Rooster and roister until dawn, drinking deeply of the sweet elixir of the good life. The only thing that nagged me now was financial. Ten bucks didn't look as big as it usually did. Ordinarily, ten bucks could have gotten me through a month of just fooling around, but the prom was the big time.

Friday night, as I sat in the kitchen before going to bed, knocking down a liverwurst on whole wheat and drinking a glass of chocolate milk, the back door slammed open and in breezed the old man, carrying his bowling bag. Friday night was his big night down at the Pin-Bowl. He was a fanatical bowler, and a good one, too. He slid the bag across the floor, pretending to lay one down the groove, his right arm held out in a graceful follow-through, right leg trailing in the classic bowling stance.

"Right in the pocket," he said with satisfaction.

"How'd you do tonight?" I asked.

"Not bad. Had a two-oh-seven game. Damn near cracked six hundred."

He opened the refrigerator and fished around for a beer, then sat down heavily, took a deep drag from the bottle, burped loudly, and said:

"Well, tomorrow's the big day, ain't it?"

"Yep," I answered. "Sure is."

"You takin' Daphne Bigelow?" he asked.

"Nah. Wanda Hickey."

"Oh, yeah? Well, you can't win 'em all. Wanda's old man is some kind of a foreman at the mill or something, ain't he?"

"I guess so."

"He drives a Studebaker Champion, don't he? The green two-door with the whitewalls."

The old man had a fine eye for cars. He judged all men by what they drove. Apparently a guy who drove a two-door Studebaker was not absolutely beyond the pale.

"Not a bad car. Except they burn oil after a while," he mused, omitting no aspects of the Studebaker.

"They used to have a weak front end. Bad kingpins." He shook his head critically, opening another beer and reaching for the rye bread.

I said nothing, lost in my own thoughts. My mother and kid brother had been in bed for an hour or so. We were, for all practical purposes, alone in the house. Next door, Mrs. Kissel threw out a pail of dishwater into the backyard with a swoosh. Her screen door slammed.

"How ya fixed for tomorrow night?" the old man asked suddenly, swirling his beer bottle around to raise the head.

"What do you mean?"

"I mean, how are ya *fixed*?"

My father never talked money to me. I got my allowance every Monday and that was that.

"Well, I've got about ten bucks."

"Hm." That was all he said.

After sitting in silence for a minute or so, he said, "You know, I always wished I coulda gone to a prom."

How can you answer something like that? He had barely gotten out of eighth grade when he had to go to work, and he never stopped for the rest of his life.

"Oh, well, what the hell." He finally answered himself.

He cut himself a slice of boiled ham and made a sandwich.

"I was really hot tonight. Got a string of six straight strikes in the second game. The old hook was movin', getting a lot of wood."

He reached into his hip pocket, took out his wallet and said:

"Look, don't tell Ma." He handed me a twenty-dollar bill.

"I had a couple of bets going on the second game, and I'm a money bowler."

He was that. No doubt of it. In his early teens, he had scrounged out a living as a pool shark, and he had never lost the touch. I took the twenty dollars, glommed onto it the way the proverbial drowning man grabs at a straw. I was so astounded at this un-precedented gesture that it never occurred to me to say thanks. He would have been embarrassed if I had. A miracle had come to pass. There was no doubt about it—the prom was going to be an unqualified gas.

The next day dawned bright and sunny, as perfect

as a June day can be—in a steel-mill town. Even the blast-furnace dust that drifted aimlessly through the soft air glowed with promise. I was out early, dusting off the car. It was going to be a top-down night. If there is anything more romantic than a convertible with the top down in June going to a prom, I'd like to hear about it. Cleopatra's barge couldn't have been much more seductive.

My kid brother, his diminutive Flash Gordon T-shirt showing a great expanse of knobby backbone and skinny belly, yapped around me as I toiled over the Ford.

"Look what you done to my T-shirt!" he whined, his runny nose atrickle. He was in the midst of his annual spring cold, which would be superseded by his summer cold, which lasted nicely to the whopper he got in the fall, which, of course, was only a prelude to his winter-long *monster* cold.

"Stay away from the fender. You're dripping on it!" I shouted angrily, shoving him away.

"Flash Gordon's only about an inch high now!"

I couldn't help laughing. It was true. Flash had shrunk, along with the shirt, which Randy had earned by doggedly eating three boxes of Wheaties, saving the boxtops and mailing them in with twenty-five cents that he had, by dint of ferocious self-denial, saved from his thirty-cent weekly allowance.

"Look, I'll get you another Flash Gordon T-shirt."

"You can't. They're not givin' 'em away no more. They're givin' away Donald Duck beanies with a propeller on top now."

"Well, then, stretch the one you got now, stupid."

"It won't stretch. It keeps getting littler."

He bounced up and down on a clothes pole, joggling the clothesline and my mother's wash. Within three seconds, she was out on the back porch.

"CUT IT OUT WITH THE CLOTHES POLE."

Suddenly, he slid off onto the ground. I went back to work, until the Ford gleamed like some rare jewel.

Then I went into the house to begin the even more laborious process of getting *myself* in shape for the evening ahead. Locking the bathroom door, I took two showers, wearing a brand-new bar of Lifebuoy down to a nub. I knew what happened to people who didn't use it; every week, little comic strips underneath *Moon Mullins* told endless tales of disastrous proms due to dreaded B.O. It would not happen to me.

I then shaved for the second time that week, using a new Gillette Blue Blade. As usual when an important shave was executed, I nicked myself nastily in several places.

"Son of a bitch," I muttered, plastering the wounds with little pieces of toilet paper.

Carefully, I went over every inch of my face, battling that age-old enemy, the blackhead, and polished off the job with a copious application of stinging Aqua Velva. Next I attacked my hair, combing and recombing, getting just the right insouciant pitch to my pride and joy, my d.a. cut. Tonight, I would be a truly magnificent specimen of lusty manhood.

Twilight was fast approaching when I emerged from the bathroom, redolent of rare aromas, pink and svelte. But the real battle had not yet begun. Laid out on my bed was my beautiful summer formal. Al was right: The elegant white coat truly gleamed in virginal splendor. Not a trace of the red stain nor the sinister hole could be detected. The coat was ready for another night of celebration, its lapels spotless, it sleeves smooth and uncreased.

Carefully, I undid the pins that festooned my pleated Monte Carlo shirt. It was the damnedest thing I had ever seen, once I got it straightened out: long, trailing gauze-like shirttails, a crinkly front that thrummed like sheet metal and a collar that seemed to be carved of white rock. I slipped it on. Panic! It had no buttons— just holes.

Rummaging around frantically in the box the suit came in, I found a cellophane envelope containing

little round black things. Ripping the envelope open.
I poured them out; there were five of them, two of
which immediately darted under the bed. From the
looks of the remaining three, they certainly weren't
buttons; but they'd have to do. Although I didn't know
it at the time, I had observed a classic maneuver
executed by at least one stud out of every set rented
with a tux. Down on my hands and knees, already
beginning to lose my Lifebuoy sheen, sweat popping
out here and there, I scrambled around for the missing
culprits.

The ordeal was well underway. Seven o'clock was
approaching with such rapidity as to be almost un-
believable. Schwartz, Clara Mae, and Wanda would
already be waiting for me, and here I was in my
drawers, crawling around on my hands and knees.
Finally, amid the dust and dead spiders under my bed,
I found the two studs cowering together behind a
hardball I'd lost three months earlier.

Back before the mirror again, I struggled to get them
in place between the concrete slits. Sweat was beginning
to show under my arms. I got two in over my breastbone
and now I tried to get the one at the collar over my
Adam's apple. It was impossible! I could feel from
deep within me several sobs beginning to form. The
more I struggled, the more hamfisted I became. Oh,
No! Two blackish thumb smudges appeared on my
snow-white collar.

"MA!" I screamed, "LOOK AT MY SHIRT!"

She rushed in from the kitchen, carrying a paring
knife and a pan of apples. "What's the matter?"

"Look!" I pointed at the telltale prints.

My kid brother cackled in delight when he saw the
trouble I was in.

"Don't touch it," she barked, taking control immediately. Dirty collars were her métier. She had
fought them all her life. She darted out of the room
and returned instantly with an artgum eraser.

"Now, hold still."

I obeyed as she carefully worked the stud in place and then artistically erased the two monstrous thumbprints. Never in my life had I experienced a collar remotely like the one that now clamped its iron grasp around my windpipe. Hard and unyielding, it dug mercilessly into my throat—a mere sample of what was to come.

"Where's your tie?" she asked. I had forgotten about that detail.

"It . . . ack . . . must be . . . in the box," I managed to gasp out. The collar had almost paralyzed my voice box.

She rummaged around and came up with the bow tie. It was black and it had two metal clips. She snapped it onto the wing collar and stood back.

"Now, look at yourself in the mirror." I didn't recognize myself.

She picked up the midnight-blue trousers and held them open, so that I could slip into them without bending over.

True to his word, Al had, indeed, taken in the seat. The pants clamped me in a viselike grip that was to damn near emasculate me before the evening was out. I sucked in my stomach, buttoned the waistband tight, zippered up the fly and stood straight as a ramrod before the mirror. I had no other choice.

"Gimme your foot."

My mother was down on all fours, pulling the silky black socks onto my feet. Then, out of a box on the bed, she removed the gleaming pair of patent-leather dancing pumps, grabbed my right foot and shoved it into one of them, using her finger as a shoehorn. I tromped down. She squealed in pain.

"I can't get my finger out!"

I hobbled around, taking her finger with me.

"STAND STILL!" she screamed.

I stood like a crane, one foot in the air, with her finger jammed deep into the heel.

"RANDY! COME HERE!" she yelled.

My kid brother, who was sulking under the daybed, ran into the room.

"PULL HIS SHOE OFF, RANDY!" She was frantic.

"What for?" he asked sullenly.

"DON'T ASK STUPID QUESTIONS. JUST DO WHAT I SAY!"

I was getting an enormous cramp in my right buttock.

"STAND STILL!" she yelled. "YOU'RE BREAKING MY FINGER!" Randy looked on impassively, observing a scene that he was later to weave into a family legend, embroidering it more and more as the years went by—making himself the hero, of course.

"RANDY! *Take off his shoe!*" Her voice quavered with pain and exasperation.

"He squirted my T-shirt."

"If you don't take off his shoe this instant, you're gonna regret it." This time, her voice was low and menacing. We both knew the tone. It was the end of the line.

Randy bent over and tugged off the shoe. My mother toppled backward in relief, rubbing her index finger, which was already blue.

"Go back under the daybed," she snapped. He scurried out of the room. I straightened out my leg—the cramp subsiding like a volcano in the marrow of my bones—and the gleaming pumps were put in place without further incident. I stood encased as in armor.

"What's this thing?" she asked from behind me. I executed a careful 180-degree turn.

"Oh, that's my cummerbund."

Her face lit up like an Italian sunrise. "A cummerbund!" She had seen Fred Astaire in many a cummerbund while he spun down marble staircases with Ginger Rogers in his arms, but it was the first actual specimen she had ever been close to. She picked it up reverently, its paisley brilliance lighting up the room like an iridescent jewel.

"How does it work?" she asked, examining it closely.

Before I could answer, she said, "Oh, I see. It has clips on the back. Hold still."

Around my waist it went. She drew it tight. The snaps clicked into place. It rode snugly halfway up my chest.

She picked up the snowy coat and held it out. I lowered my arms into it and straightened up. She darted around to the front, closed the single button, and there I stood—Adonis!

Posing before the full-length mirror on the bathroom door, I noted the rich accent of my velvet stripes, the gleam of my pumps, the magnificent dash and sparkle of my high-fashion cummerbund. What a sight! What a feeling! This is the way life should be. This is what it's all about.

I heard my mother call out from the next room: "Hey, what's this thing?" She came out holding a cellophane bag containing a maroon object.

"Oh, that's my boutonniere."

"Your what?"

"It's a thing for the lapel. Like a fake flower."

It was the work of an instant to install my elegant wool carnation. It was the crowning touch. I was so overwhelmed that I didn't care about the fact that it didn't match my black tie, as Al had promised. With the cummerbund I was wearing, no one would notice, anyway.

Taking my leave as Cary Grant would have done, I sauntered out the front door, turned to give my mother a jaunty wave—just in time for her to call me back to pick up Wanda's corsage, which I'd left on the front-hall table.

Slipping carefully into the front seat with the cellophane-topped box safely beside me, I leaned forward slightly, to avoid wrinkling the back of my coat, started the motor up and shoved off into the warm summer night. A soft June moon hung overhead. The Ford purred like a kitten. When I pulled up before Wanda's house, it was lit up from top to bottom.

Even before my brakes had stopped squealing, she was out on the porch, her mother fluttering about her, her father lurking in the background, beaming.

With stately tread, I moved up the walk; my pants were so tight that if I'd taken one false step, God knows what would have happened. In my sweaty, Aqua Velva–scented palm, I clutched the ritual largess in its shiny box.

Wanda wore a long turquoise taffeta gown, her milky skin and golden hair radiating in the glow of the porch light. This was *not* the old Wanda. For one thing, she didn't have her glasses on, and her eyes were unnaturally large and liquid, the way the true myopia victim's always are.

"Gee, thanks for the orchid," she whispered. Her voice sounded strained. In accordance with the tribal custom, she, too, was being mercilessly clamped by straps and girdles.

Her mother, an almost exact copy of Wanda, only slightly puffy here and there, said, "You'll take care of her now, won't you?"

"Now, Emily, don't start yapping," her old man muttered in the darkness. "They're not kids anymore."

They stood in the door as we drove off through the soft night toward Schwartz' house, our conversation stilted, our excitement almost at the boiling point. Schwartz rushed out of his house, his white coat like a ghost in the blackness, his hair agleam with Brylcreem, and surrounded by a palpable aura of Lifebuoy.

Five minutes later, Clara Mae piled into the back seat beside him, carefully holding up her daffodil-yellow skirts, her long slender neck arched. She, too, wasn't wearing her glasses. I had never realized that a good speller could be so pretty. Schwartz, a good half head shorter, laughed nervously as we tooled on toward the Cherrywood Country Club. From all over town, other cars, polished and waxed, carried the rest of the junior class to their great trial by fire.

The club nestled amid the rolling hills, where the

Sinclair oil aroma was only barely detectable. Parking the car in the lot, we threaded our way through the starched and crinolined crowd—the girls' girdles creaking in unison—to the grand ballroom. Japanese lanterns danced in the breeze through the open doors to the garden, bathing the dance floor in a fairy-tale glow.

I found myself saying things like, "Why, hello there, Albert, how are you?" And, "Yes, I believe the weather is perfect." Only Flick, the unregenerate Philistine, failed to rise to the occasion. Already rumpled in his summer formal, he made a few tasteless wisecracks as Mickey Eisley and his Magic Music Makers struck up the sultry sounds that had made them famous in every steel-mill town that ringed Lake Michigan. Dark and sensuous, the dance floor engulfed as all. I felt tall, slim, and beautiful, not realizing at the time that everybody feels that way wearing a white coat and rented pants. I could see myself standing on a mysterious balcony, a lonely, elegant figure, looking out over the lights of some exotic city, a scene of sophisticated gaiety behind me.

There was a hushed moment when Mickey Eisley stood in the baby spot, his wavy hair shining, before a microphone shaped like a chromium bullet.

"All right, boys and girls." The metallic ring of feedback framed his words in an echoing nimbus. "And now something really romantic. A request: *When the Swallows Come Back to Capistrano*. We're going to turn the lights down for this one."

Oh, wow! The lights faded even lower. Only the Japanese lanterns glowed dimly—red, green, yellow, and blue—in the enchanted darkness. It was unquestionably the high point of my existence.

Wanda and I began to maneuver around the floor. My sole experience in dancing had been gained from reading Arthur Murray ads and practicing with a pillow for a partner behind the locked door of the bathroom. As we shuffled across the floor, I could see the black footprints before my eyes, marching on a white page: 1-2-3; then the white one that said, "Pause."

Back and forth, up and down, we moved metronomically. My box step was so square that I went in little right angles for weeks afterward. The wool carnation rode high up on my lapel and was beginning to scratch my cheek, and an insistent itch began to nag at my right shoulder. There was some kind of wire or horsehair or something in the shoulder pad that was beginning to bore its way into my flesh.

By now, my dashing concrete collar, far from having wilted, had set into the consistency of carborundum, and its incessant abrasive action had removed a wide strip of skin encircling my neck. As for my voice—due to the manic strangulation of the collar, it was now little more than a hoarse croak.

"When the swallows . . . retuuurrrrrn to Capistraaaa-aaaano . . ." mooed the drummer, who doubled as the band's romantic vocalist.

I began to notice Wanda's orchid leering up at me from her shoulder. It was the most repulsive flower I had ever seen. At least fourteen inches across, it looked like some kind of overgrown Venus's-flytrap waiting for the right moment to strike. Deep purple, with an obscene yellow tongue that stuck straight out of it, and greenish knobs on the end, it clashed almost audibly with her turquoise dress. It looked like it was breathing, and it clung to her shoulder as if with claws.

As I glided back and forth in my graceful box step, my left shoulder began to develop an itch that helped take my mind off of the insane itch in my right shoulder, which was beginning to feel like an army of hungry soldier ants on the march. The contortions I made to relieve the agony were camouflaged nicely by a short sneezing fit brought on by the orchid, which was exhaling directly into my face. So was Wanda, with a heady essence of Smith Brothers cough drops and sauerkraut.

"When the deeeep purpullllll falllllllls . . . Over sleeeeepy gaaardennnn walllls . . ." warbled the vocalist into his microphone, with which he seemed to be dancing the tango. The loudspeakers rattled in three-quarter time as Wanda started to sweat through her taffeta. I felt it running down her back. My own back was already so wet you could read the label on my undershirt right through the dinner jacket.

Back and forth we trudged doggedly across the crowded floor. Another Arthur Murray ad man, Schwartz was doing exactly the same step with Clara Mae directly behind me. We were all in a four-part lock step. As I hit the lower left-hand footprint in my square—the one marked "Pause"—he was hitting the upper right-hand corner of his square. Each time we did that, our elbows dug smartly into each other's ribs.

The jungle fragrance of the orchid was getting riper by the minute and the sweat, which had now saturated my jockey shorts, was pouring down my legs in rivulets. My soaked cummerbund turned two shades darker. So that she shouldn't notice, I pulled Wanda closer to me. Sighing, she hugged me back. Wanda was the vaguely chubby type of girl that was so popular at the time. Like Judy Garland, by whom she was heavily influenced, she strongly resembled a pink beach ball—but a *cute* beach ball, soft and rubbery. I felt bumpy things under her taffeta gown, with little hooks and knobs. Schwartz caught me a nasty shot in the rib cage just as I bent over to kiss her lightly on the bridge of her nose. It tasted salty. She looked up at me, her great liquid myopic eyes catching the reflection of the red and green lanterns overhead.

During a brief intermission, Schwartz and I carried paper cups dripping syrupy punch back to the girls, who had just spent some time in the ladies' room struggling unsuccessfully to repair the damage of the first half. As we were sipping, a face from my dim past floated by from out of nowhere—haughty, alabaster, green-eyed, dangerous.

"Hi, Daph," I muttered, spilling a little punch on my

gleaming pumps, which had turned during the past
hour into a pair of iron maidens.

"Oh, Howard." She spoke in the breathy, sexy way
that such girls always have at proms. "I'd like you to
meet Budge. Budge Cameron. He's at Princeton." A
languid figure, probably born in a summer formal,
loomed overhead.

"Budge, this is Howard."

"Hiya, fella." It was the first time I had heard the
tight, nasal, swinging-jaw accent of the true Prince-
tonian. It was not to be the last.

They were gone. Funny, I couldn't even remember
actually dating her, I reflected, as the lights dimmed
once again. We swung back into action. They opened
with *Sleepy Lagoon.* 1-2-3- pause . . . 1-2-3-pause.

It was certain now. I had broken out in a raging
rash. I felt it spreading like lava across my shoulder
blades under the sweat. The horsehair, meanwhile, had
penetrated my chest cavity and was working its way
toward a vital organ. Trying manfully to ignore it, I
stared fixedly at the tiny turquoise ribbon that held
Wanda's golden ponytail in place. With troubles of
her own, she looked with an equally level gaze at my
maroon-wool carnation, which by this time had wilted
into a clump of lint.

All of a sudden, it was all over. The band played
Good Night, Sweetheart and we were out—into a
driving rain. A violent cloudburst had begun just as we
reached the door. My poor little car, the pride and joy
of my life, was outside in the lot. With the top down.

None of us, of course, had an umbrella. We stood
under the canopy as the roaring thunderstorm raged
on. It wasn't going to stop.

"You guys stay here. I'll get the car," I said finally.
After all, I was in charge.

Plunging into the downpour, I sloshed through the
puddles and finally reached the Ford. She must have
had at least a foot of water in her already. Hair
streaming down over my eyes, soaked to the skin, and

muddied to the knees. I bailed it out with a coffee can from the trunk, slid behind the wheel and pressed the automatic-top lever. Smooth as silk, it began to lift—and stuck halfway up. As the rain poured down in sheets and the lightning flashed, I pounded on the relays, furiously switched the lever off and on. I could see the country club dimly through the downpour. Finally, the top groaned and flapped into place. I threw down the snaps, rolled up the windows and turned on the ignition; the battery was dead. The strain of hoisting that goddamn top had drained it dry. I yelled out the window at a passing car. It was Flick in his Chevy.

"GIMME A PUSH! MY BATTERY'S DEAD!"

This had never, to my knowledge, happened to Fred Astaire. And if it rained on Gene Kelly, he just sang.

Flick expertly swung his Chevy around and slammed into my trunk as I eased her into gear, and when she started to roll, the Ford shuddered and caught. Flick backed up and was gone, hollering out the window:

"SEE YOU AT THE ROOSTER."

Wanda, Schwartz, and Clara Mae piled in on the damp, soggy seats and we took off. Do you know what happens to a maroon-wool carnation on a white-serge lapel in a heavy June downpour in the Midwest, where it rains not water but carbolic acid from the steel-mill fallout? I had a dark, wide, spreading maroon stripe that went all the way down to the bottom of my white coat. My French cuffs were covered with grease from fighting the top, and I had cracked a thumbnail, which was beginning to throb.

Undaunted, we slogged intrepidly through the rain toward the Red Rooster. Wedged against my side, Wanda looked up at me—oblivious to the elements—with luminous love eyes. She was truly an incurable romantic. Schwartz wisecracked in the back seat and Clara giggled from time to time. The savage tribal rite was nearing its final and most vicious phase.

We arrived at the Red Rooster, already crowded

with other candidates for adulthood. A giant red neon
rooster with a blue neon tail that flicked up and down
in the rain set the tone for this glamorous establishment. An aura of undefined sin was always connected
with the name Red Rooster. Sly winks, nudgings, and
adolescent cacklings about what purportedly went on
at the Rooster made it the "in" spot for such a
momentous revel. Its waiters were rumored really to be
secret henchmen of the Mafia. But the only thing we
knew for sure about the Rooster was that anybody on
the far side of seven years old could procure any known
drink without question.

The decor ran heavily to red-checkered-oilcloth table
covers and plastic violets, and the musical background
was provided by a legendary jukebox that stood a full
seven feet high, featuring red and blue cascading
waterfalls that gushed endlessly through its voluptuous
façade. In full 200-watt operation, it could be *felt*, if
not clearly heard, as far north as Gary and as far south
as Kankakee. A triumph of American aesthetics.

Surging with anticipation, I guided Wanda through
the uproarious throng of my peers. Schwartz and Clara
Mae trailed behind, exchanging ribald remarks with
the gang.

We occupied the only remaining table. Immediately,
a beady-eyed waiter, hair glistening with Vaseline Hair
Oil, sidled over and hovered like a vulture. Quickly
distributing the famous Red Rooster Ala Carte Deluxe
Menu, he stood back, smirking, and waited for us to
impress our dates.

"Can I bring you anything to drink, gentlemen?"
he said, heavily accenting the "gentlemen."

My first impulse was to order my favorite drink of
the period, a bottled chocolate concoction called Kayo,
the Wonder Drink; but remembering that better things
were expected of me on prom night, I said, in my deep-
est voice, "Uh . . . make mine . . . bourbon."

Schwartz grunted in admiration. Wanda ogled me
with great, swimming, lovesick eyes. Bourbon was the

only drink that I had actually heard of. My old man ordered it often down at the Bluebird Tavern. I had always wondered what it tasted like. I was soon to find out.

"How will you have it, sir?"

"Well, in a glass, I guess." I had failed to grasp the subtlety of his question, but the waiter snorted in appreciation of my humorous sally.

"Rocks?" he continued.

Rocks? I had heard about getting your rocks, but never in a restaurant. Oh, well, what the hell.

"Sure," I said. "Why not?"

All around me, the merrymaking throng was swinging into high gear. Carried away by it all, I added a phrase I had heard my old man use often: "And make it a triple." I had some vague idea that this was a brand or something.

"A *triple?* Yes, sir." His eyes snapped wide—in respect, I gathered. He knew he was in the presence of a serious drinker.

The waiter turned his gaze in Schwartz' direction. "And you, sir?"

"Make it the same." Schwartz had never been a leader.

The die was cast. Pink ladies, at the waiter's suggestion, were ordered for the girls, and we then proceeded to scan the immense menu with feigned disinterest. When the waiter returned with our drinks, I ordered —for reasons that even today I am unable to explain— lamb chops, yellow turnips, mashed potatoes and gravy, a side dish of the famous Red Rooster Roquefort Italian Cole Slaw—and a strawberry shortcake. The others wisely decided to stick with their drinks.

Munching bread sticks, Wanda, Schwartz, Clara, and I engaged in sophisticated postprom repartee. Moment by moment, I felt my strength and maturity, my dashing bonhomie, my clean-cut handsomeness enveloping my friends in its benevolent warmth. Schwartz, too, seemed to scintillate as never before. Clara giggled and

Wanda sighed, overcome by the romance of it all. Even when Flick, sitting three tables away, clipped Schwartz behind the left ear with a poppyseed roll, our urbanity remained unruffled.

Before me reposed a sparkling tumbler of beautiful amber liquid, ice cubes bobbing merrily on its surface, a plastic swizzle stick sporting an enormous red rooster sticking out at a jaunty angle. Schwartz was similarly equipped. And the fluffy pink ladies looked lovely in the reflected light of the pulsating jukebox.

I had seen my old man deal with just this sort of situation. Raising my beaded glass, I looked around at my companions and said suavely, "Well, here's mud in yer eye." Clara giggled; Wanda sighed dreamily, now totally in love with this man of the world who sat across from her on this, our finest night.

"Yep," Schwartz parried wittily, hoisting his glass high and slopping a little bourbon on his pants as he did so.

Swiftly, I brought the bourbon to my lips, intending to down it in a single devil-may-care draught, the way Gary Cooper used to do in the Silver Dollar Saloon. I did, and Schwartz followed suit. Down it went—a screaming 90-proof rocket searing savagely down my gullet. For an instant, I sat stunned, unable to comprehend what had happened. Eyes watering copiously, I had a brief urge to sneeze, but my throat seemed to be paralyzed. Wanda and Clara Mae swam before my misted vision; and Schwartz seemed to have disappeared under the table. He popped up again—face beet-red, eyes bugging, jaw slack, tongue lolling.

"Isn't this romantic? Isn't this the most wonderful night in all our lives? I will forever treasure the memories of this wonderful night." From far off, echoing as from some subterranean tunnel, I heard Wanda speaking.

Deep down in the pit of my stomach, I felt crackling flames licking at my innards. I struggled to reply, to maintain my élan, my fabled *savoir-faire*. "Urk . . . urk

. . . yeah," I finally managed with superhuman effort.

Wanda swam hazily into focus. She was gazing across the table at me with adoring eyes.

"Another, gents?" The waiter was back, still smirking. Schwartz nodded dumbly. I just sat there, afraid to move. An instant later, two more triple bourbons materialized in front of us.

Clara raised her pink lady high and said reverently, "Let's drink to the happiest night of our lives."

There was no turning back. Another screamer rocketed down the hatch. For an instant, it seemed as though this one wasn't going to be as lethal as the first, but the room suddenly tilted sideways. I felt torrents of cold sweat pouring from my forehead. Clinging to the edge of the table, I watched as Schwartz gagged across from me. Flick, I noticed, had just chugalugged his third rum-and-Coke and was eating a cheeseburger with the works.

The conflagration deep inside me was now clearly out of control. My feet were smoking; my diaphragm heaved convulsively, jiggling my cummerbund; and Schwartz began to shrink, his face alternating between purple-red and chalk-white, his eyes black holes staring fixedly at the ketchup bottle. He sat stock-still. Wanda, meanwhile, cooed on ecstatically—but I was beyond understanding what she was saying. Faster and faster, in ever-widening circles, the room, the jukebox, the crowd swirled dizzily about me. In all the excitement of preparations for the prom, I realized that I hadn't eaten a single thing all day.

Out of the maelstrom, a plate mysteriously appeared before me; paper-pantied lamb chops hissing in bubbling grease, piled yellow turnips, gray mashed potatoes awash in rich brown gravy. Maybe this would help, I thought incoherently. Grasping my knife and fork as firmly as I could, I poised to whack off a piece of meat. Suddenly, the landscape listed forty-five degrees to starboard and the chop I was about to attack skidded off my plate—plowing a swath through the mashed potatoes—and right into the aisle.

Pretending not to notice, I addressed myself to the remaining chop, which slid around, eluding my grasp, until I managed to skewer it with my fork. Hacking off a chunk, I jammed it fiercely mouthward, missing my target completely. Still impaled on my fork, the chop slithered over my cheekbone, spraying gravy as it went, all over my white lapels. On the next try, I had better luck, and finally I managed to get the whole chop down.

To my surprise, I didn't feel any better. Maybe the turnips will help, I thought. Lowering my head to within an inch of the plate to prevent embarrassing mishaps, I shoveled them in—but the flames within only fanned higher and higher. I tried the potatoes and gravy. My legs began to turn cold. I wolfed down the Red Rooster Roquefort Italian Cole Slaw. My stomach began to rise like a helium balloon, bobbing slowly up the alimentary canal.

My nose low over the heaping dish of strawberry shortcake, piled high with whipped cream and running with juice, I knew at last for a dead certainty what I had to do before it happened right here in front of everybody. I struggled to my feet. A strange rubbery numbness had struck my extremities. I tottered from chair to chair, grasping for the wall. There was a buzzing in my ears.

Twenty seconds later, I was on my knees, gripping the bowl of the john like a life preserver in pitching seas. Schwartz, imitating me as usual, lay almost prostrate on the tiles beside me, his body racked with heaving sobs. Lamb chops, bourbon, turnips, mashed potatoes, cole slaw—all of it came rushing out of me in a great roaring torrent—out of my mouth, my nose, my ears, my very soul. Then Schwartz opened up, and we took turns retching and shuddering. A head thrust itself between us directly into the pot. It was Flick moaning wretchedly. Up came the cheeseburger, the rum-and-Cokes, pretzels, potato chips, punch, gumdrops, a corned-beef sandwich, a fingernail or two—everything he'd eaten for the last week. For long minutes, the three of us lay there limp and quivering, smelling to high heaven, too weak to get up. It was the absolute high point of the junior prom; the rest was anticlimax.

Finally, we returned to the table, ashen-faced and shaking. Schwartz, his coat stained and rumpled, sat Zombie-like across from me. The girls didn't say much. Pink ladies just aren't straight bourbon.

But our little group played the scene out bravely to the end. My dinner jacket was now even more redolent and disreputable than when I'd first seen it on the hanger at Al's. And my bow tie, which had hung for a while by one clip, had somehow disappeared completely, perhaps flushed into eternity with all the rest. But as time wore on, my hearing and eyesight began slowly to return; my legs began to lose their rubberiness and the room slowly resumed its even keel—at least even enough to consider getting up and leaving. The waiter seemed to know. He returned as if on cue, bearing a slip of paper.

"The damages, gentlemen."

Taking the old man's twenty dollars out of my wallet, I handed it to him with as much of a flourish as I could muster. There wouldn't have been any point in looking over the check; I wouldn't have been able to read it, anyway. In one last attempt to recoup my cosmopolitan image, I said offhandedly, "Keep the change." Wanda beamed in unconcealed ecstasy.

The drive home in the damp car was not quite the same as the one that had begun the evening so many weeks earlier. Our rapidly fermenting coats made the enclosed air rich and gamy, and Schwartz, who had stopped belching, sat with head pulled low between his shoulder blades, staring straight ahead. Only the girls preserved the joyousness of the occasion. Women always survive.

In a daze, I dropped off Schwartz and Clara Mae

and drove in silence toward Wanda's home, the faint light of dawn beginning to show in the east.

We stood on her porch for the last ritual encounter. A chill dawn wind rustled the lilac bushes.

"This was the most wonderful, wonderful night of my whole life. I always dreamed the prom would be like this," breathed Wanda, gazing passionately up into my watering eyes.

"Me, too," was all I could manage.

I knew what was expected of me now. Her eyes closed dreamily. Swaying slightly, I leaned forward—and the faint odor of sauerkraut from her parted lips coiled slowly up to my nostrils. This was not in the script. I knew I had better get off that porch fast, or else. Backpedaling desperately and down the stairs, I blurted, "Bye!" and—fighting down my rising gorge—clamped my mouth tight, leaped into the Ford, burned rubber, and tore off into the dawn. Two blocks away, I squealed to a stop alongside a vacant lot containing only a huge Sherwin-Williams paint sign. WE COVER THE WORLD, it aptly read. In the blessed darkness behind the sign, concealed from prying eyes, I completed the final rite of the ceremony.

The sun was just rising as I swung the car up the driveway and eased myself quietly into the kitchen. The old man, who was going fishing that morning, sat at the enamel table sipping black coffee. He looked up as I came in. I was in no mood for idle chatter.

"You look like you had a hell of a prom," was all he said.

"I sure did."

The yellow kitchen light glared harshly on my muddy pants, my maroon-streaked, vomit-stained white coat, my cracked fingernail, my greasy shirt.

"You want anything to eat?" he asked sardonically.

At the word "eat," my stomach heaved convulsively. I shook my head numbly.

"That's what I thought," he said. "Get some sleep.

You'll feel better in a couple of days, when your head stops banging."

He went back to reading his paper. I staggered into my bedroom, dropping bits of clothing as I went. My soggy Hollywood paisley cummerbund, the veteran of another gala night, was flung beneath my dresser as I toppled into bed. My brother muttered in his sleep across the room. He was still a kid. But his time would come.

Judith Viorst

Judith Viorst is a humorous poet, journalist, writer of children's books, and frequent contributor to newspapers and magazines. A native of Newark, New Jersey, she now lives in Washington, D.C., with her husband, journalist Milton Viorst, and three sons. Mrs. Viorst launched her writing career when she was seven years old, but it wasn't until she married and began writing about herself, her husband, her marriage, and her children that she achieved publishing success. Her wry observations of the American domestic scene balance loving acceptance with subtle irony. Her books include *People and Other Aggravations* and *How Did I Get To Be Forty . . . & Other Atrocities*.

MONEY

Once I aspired to
Humble black turtleneck sweaters
And spare unheated rooms
With the Kama Sutra, a few madrigals, and
Great literature and philosophy.

Once I considered money
Something to be against
On the grounds that
Credit cards,
Installment-plan buying,
And a joint checking account
Could never coexist with
Great literature and philosophy.

Once I believed
That the only kind of marriage I could respect
Was a spiritual relationship
Between two wonderfully spiritual human beings
Who would never argue about money
Because they would be too busy arguing about
Great literature and philosophy.

I changed my mind,
Having discovered that

Spiritual is hard without the cash
To pay the plumber to unstop the sink
And pay a lady to come clean and iron

So every other Friday I can think about
Great literature and philosophy.

No one ever offers us a choice
Between the Kama Sutra and a yacht.
We're always selling out for diaper service
And other drab necessities that got ignored in
Great literature and philosophy.

A jug of wine, a loaf of bread, and thou
No longer will suffice. I must confess
My consciousness is frequently expanded
By Diners' Club, American Express, and things
   undreamed of in
Great literature and philosophy.

I saw us walking hand-in-hand through life,
But now it's clear we really need two cars.
I looked with such contempt at power mowers,
And now, alas, that power mower's ours.
It seems I'm always reaching for my charge plates,
When all I'd planned to reach for were the stars,
Great literature and philosophy.

TRUE LOVE

It's true love because
I put on eyeliner and a concerto and make pungent
    observations about the great issues of the day
Even when there's no one here but him,
And because
I do not resent watching the Green Bay Packers
Even though I am philosophically opposed to football,
And because
When he is late for dinner and I know he must be
    either having an affair or lying dead in the middle of
    the street,
I always hope he's dead.

It's true love because
If he said quit drinking martinis but I kept drinking
    them and the next morning I couldn't get out of bed,
He wouldn't tell me he told me,
And because
He is willing to wear unironed undershorts
Out of respect for the fact that I am philosophically
    opposed to ironing
And because
If his mother was drowning and I was drowning and he
    had to choose one of us to save,
He says he'd save me.

It's true love because
When he went to San Francisco on business while I had
    to stay home with the painters and the exterminator
    and the baby who was getting the chicken pox,

He understood why I hated him,
And because
When I said that playing the stock market was juvenile
 and irresponsible and then the stock I wouldn't let
 him buy went up twenty-six points
I understood why he hated me,
And because
Despite cigarette cough, tooth decay, acid indigestion,
 dandruff, and other features of married life that tend
 to dampen the fires of passion,
We still feel something
We can call
True love.

Woody Allen
[1935-   ]

Woody Allen began his comic career as a teenager by sending one-liners to a television host show personality. A native New Yorker, he attended New York University and City College, and became a writer for some of the leading comic entertainers of the 1950s. Eventually he became a performer himself, first in nightclubs and on television, and then in the movies as well. He acquired a devoted following with his low-key, deadpan observations and his descriptions of his hilariously neurotic woes. He has a particular genius for pursuing an inane subject with utter but preposterous seriousness to an outrageous conclusion. Today he has to his credit plays, records, TV specials and books. He is probably best-known for his films—*Take the Money and Run, Sleeper, Love and Death,* and *Annie Hall* among others which he has written, directed, and starred in. He also regularly contributes humorous pieces to leading periodicals.

THE UFO MENACE

UFOs are back in the news, and it is high time we took a serious look at this phenomenon. (Actually, the time is ten past eight, so not only are we a few minutes late but I'm hungry.) Up until now, the entire subject of flying saucers has been mostly associated with kooks or oddballs. Frequently, in fact, observers will admit to being a member of both groups. Still, persistent sightings by responsible individuals have caused the Air Force and the scientific community to reexamine a once skeptical attitude, and the sum of two hundred dollars has now been allocated for a comprehensive study of the phenomenon. The question is: Is anything out there? And if so, do they have ray guns?

All UFOs may not prove to be of extraterrestrial origin, but experts do agree that any glowing cigar-shaped aircraft capable of rising straight up at twelve thousand miles per second would require the kind of maintenance and sparkplugs available only on Pluto. If these objects are indeed from another planet, then the civilization that designed them must be millions of years more advanced than our own. Either that or they are very lucky. Professor Leon Speciman postulates a civilization in outer space that is more advanced than ours by approximately fifteen minutes. This, he feels, gives them a great advantage over us, since they needn't rush to get to appointments.

Dr. Brackish Menzies, who works at the Mount Wilson Observatory, or else is under observation at the Mount Wilson Mental Hospital (the letter is not clear), claims that travelers moving at close to the speed of light would require many millions of years to get here, even from the nearest solar system, and, judging from the shows on Broadway, the trip would hardly be worth it. (It is impossible to travel faster than light, and certainly not desirable, as one's hat keeps blowing off.)

Interestingly, according to modern astronomers, space is finite. This is a very comforting thought—particularly for people who can never remember where they have left things. The key factor in thinking about the universe, however, is that it is expanding and will one day break apart and disappear. That is why if the girl in the office down the hall has some good points but perhaps not all the qualities you require it's best to compromise.

The most frequently asked question about the UFOs is: If saucers come from outer space, why have their pilots not attempted to make contact with us, instead of hovering mysteriously over deserted areas? My own theory is that for creatures from another solar system "hovering" may be a socially acceptable mode of relating. It may, indeed, be pleasurable. I myself once hovered over an eighteen-year-old actress for six months and had the best time of my life. It should also be recalled that when we talk of "life" on other planets we are frequently referring to amino acids, which are never very gregarious, even at parties.

Most people tend to think of UFOs as a modern problem, but could they be a phenomenon that man has been aware of for centuries? (To us a century seems quite long, particularly if you are holding an I.O.U., but by astronomical standards it is over in a second. For that reason, it is always best to carry a toothbrush and be ready to leave on a moment's notice.) Scholars now tell us that the sighting of unidentified flying objects dates as far back as Biblical times. For instance, there is a passage in the Book of Leviticus that reads, "And an great and silver ball appeared over the Assyrian Armies, and in all of Babylonia there was wailing and gnashing of teeth, till the Prophets bade the multitudes get a grip on themselves and shape up."

Was this phenomenon related to one described years later by Parmenides: "Three orange objects did appear suddenly in the heavens and did circle midtown Athens, hovering over the baths and causing several of our wisest philosophers to grab for towels"? And, again, were those "orange objects" similar to what is described in a recently discovered twelfth-century Saxon-church manuscript: "A lauch lauched he; wer richt laith to weet a cork-heild schonne; whilst a red balle lang owre swam aboone. I thank you, ladies and gentlemen"?

This last account was taken by medieval clergy to signify that the world was coming to an end, and there was great disappointment when Monday came and everyone had to go back to work.

Finally, and most convincingly, in 1822 Goethe himself notes a strange celestial phenomenon. "En route home from the Leipzig Anxiety Festival," he wrote, "I was crossing a meadow, when I chanced to look up and saw several fiery red balls suddenly appear in the southern sky. They descended at a great rate of speed and began chasing me. I screamed that I was a genius and consequently could not run very fast, but my words were wasted. I became enraged and shouted imprecations at them, whereupon they flew away frightened. I related this story to Beethoven, not realizing he had already gone deaf, and he smiled and nodded and said, 'Right.'"

As a general rule, careful on-the-scene investigations disclose that most "unidentified" flying objects are quite ordinary phenomena, such as weather balloons, meteorites, satellites, and even once a man named Lewis Mandelbaum, who blew off the roof of the World Trade Center. A typical "explained" incident is the one reported by Sir Chester Ramsbottom, on June 5, 1961, in Shropshire: "I was driving along the road at 2 A.M. and saw a cigar-shaped object that seemed to be tracking my car. No matter which way I drove, it stayed with me, turning sharply at right angles. It was a fierce, glowing red, and in spite of twisting and turning the car at high speed I could not lose it. I became alarmed and began sweating. I let out a shriek of terror and apparently fainted, but awoke in a hospital, miraculously unharmed." Upon investigation, experts determined that the "cigar-shaped object" was Sir Chester's nose. Naturally, all his evasive actions could not lose it, since it was attached to his face.

Another explained incident began in late April of 1972, with a report from Major General Curtis Memling, of Andrews Air Force Base: "I was walking across a field one night and suddenly I saw a large silver disc in the sky. It flew over me, not fifty feet above my head, and repeatedly described aerodynamic patterns impossible for any normal aircraft. Suddenly it accelerated and shot away at terrific speed."

Investigators became suspicious when they noticed that General Memling could not describe this incident without giggling. He later admitted he had just come from a showing of the film "War of the Worlds," at the post movie theater, and "got a very big kick out of it." Ironically, General Memling reported another UFO sighting in 1976, but it was soon discovered that he, too, had become fixated on Sir Chester Ramsbottom's nose —an occurrence that caused consternation in the Air Force and eventually led to General Memling's court-martial.

If most UFO sightings can be satisfactorily explained, what of those few which cannot? Following are some of the most mystifying examples of "unsolved" en-counters, the first reported by a Boston man in May, 1969: "I was walking by the beach with my wife. She's not a very attractive woman. Rather overweight. In fact, I was pulling her on a dolly at the time. Suddenly I looked up and saw a huge white saucer that seemed to be descending at great speed. I guess I panicked, because I dropped the rope on my wife's dolly and began running. The saucer passed directly over my head and I heard an eerie, metallic voice say, 'Call your service.' When I got home, I phoned my answering service and received a message that my brother Ralph had moved and to forward all his mail to Neptune. I never saw him again. My wife suffered a severe breakdown over the incident and now cannot converse without using a hand puppet."

From I. M. Axelbank, of Athens, Georgia, February, 1971: "I am an experienced pilot and was flying my private Cessna from New Mexico to Amarillo, Texas, to bomb some people whose religious persuasion I do not wholly agree with, when I noticed an object flying alongside me. At first I thought it was another plane, until it emitted a green beam of light, forcing my plane to drop eleven thousand feet in four seconds and causing my toupee to snap off my head and tear a two-foot hole in the roof. I repeatedly called for help on my radio, but for some reason could only get the old 'Mr. Anthony' program. The UFO came very close to my plane again and then shot away at blinding speed. By this time I had lost my bearings and was forced to make an emergency landing on the turnpike. I continued the trip in the plane on the ground and only got into trouble when I tried to run a toll booth and broke off my wings."

One of the eeriest accounts occurred in August, 1975, to a man on Montauk Point, in Long Island: "I was in bed at my beach house, but could not sleep because of some fried chicken in the icebox that I felt entitled to. I waited till my wife dropped off, and tiptoed into the kitchen. I remember looking at the clock. It was precisely four-fifteen. I'm quite certain of this, because our kitchen clock has not worked in twenty-one years and is always at that time. I also noticed that our dog, Judas, was acting funny. He was standing up on his hind legs and singing, 'I Enjoy Being a Girl.' Suddenly the room turned bright orange. At first, I thought my wife had caught me eating between meals and set fire to the house. Then I looked out the window, where to my amazement I saw a gigantic cigar-shaped aircraft hovering just over the treetops in the yard and emitting an orange glow. I stood transfixed for what must have been several hours, though our clock still read four-fifteen, so it was difficult to tell. Finally, a large, mechanical claw extended from the aircraft and snatched the two pieces of chicken from my hand and quickly retreated. The machine then rose and, accelerating at great speed, vanished into the sky. When I reported the incident to the Air Force, they told me that what I had seen was a flock of birds. When I protested, Colonel Quincy Bascomb personally promised that the Air Force would return the two pieces of chicken. To this day, I have only received one piece."

Finally, an account in January, 1977, by two Louisiana factory workers: "Roy and I was catfishing in the bog. I enjoy the bog, as does Roy. We was not drinking, although we had brought with us a gallon of methyl chloride, which we both favor with either a twist of lemon or a small onion. Anyways, at about midnight we looked up and saw a bright-yellow sphere descend into the bog. At first Roy mistook it for a whooping crane and took a shot at it, but I said, 'Roy, that ain't no crane, 'cause it's got no beak.' That's how you can tell a crane. Roy's son Gus has a beak, you know, and thinks he's a crane. Anyways, all of a sudden this door slides open and several creatures emerge. These creatures looked like little portable radios with teeth and short hair. They also had legs, although where the toes usually are they had wheels. The creatures motioned to me to come forward, which I did, and they injected me with a fluid that caused me to smile and act like Bopeep. They spoke with one another in a strange tongue, which sounded like when you back your car over a fat person. They took me aboard the aircraft and gave me what seemed to be a complete physical examination. I went along with it, as I had not had a checkup in two years. By now they had mastered my own language, but they still made simple mistakes like using 'hermeneutics,' when they meant 'heuristic.' They told me they were from another galaxy and were here to tell the earth that we must learn to live in peace or they will return with special weapons and laminate every first-born male. They said they would get the results of my blood test back in a couple of days and if I didn't hear from them I could go ahead and marry Clair."

ABOUT THE ANTHOLOGISTS

M. JERRY WEISS, professor of communications at Jersey City State College, is a nationally known authority on communications, media, reading and language arts. He received his M.A. and Ed.D. from Teachers College, Columbia University. Dr. Weiss has worked in rural, suburban and inner-city schools as classroom teacher, college professor and school consultant. He is a past president of the College Reading Association and is currently president of ALAN (Assembly on Literature for Adolescents, National Council of Teachers of English).

HELEN S. WEISS has honed her sense of humor raising four children and has been active in community and synagogue activities. She served on the Montclair Citizen's Advisory Committee for Titles One and Seven.

START A COLLECTION

With Bantam's fiction anthologies, you can begin almos
anywhere. Choose from science fiction, classic litera
ture, modern short stories, mythology, and more—all b
both new and established writers in America and aroun
the world.